FISH FAMILIES

Find the stickers for page 1.
Place each sticker next to the fish it matches.

1

This  is **bigger** than this .
Find the stickers for page 2. Place each sticker with the correct group.
Circle the **bigger** bike in each row.

BOAT RACE

This 🐟 is **smaller** than this 🐟.
Find the stickers for page 3. Place each sticker with the correct group.
Circle the **smaller** boat in each row.

Size Differentiation

Find the stickers for page 4.
Place each shoe sticker in the correct box.

Color the big shells **purple**.
Color the small shells orange.

Matching; Size Differentiation

Draw a line from each swimmer to the correct beach towel.

How should this beach towel look?
Draw your own design.

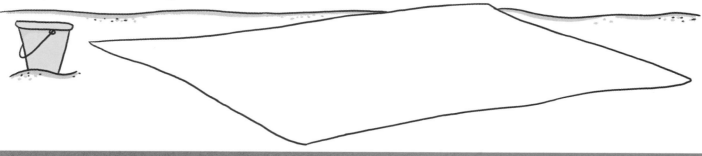

Working with Patterns

Today's Events
Parade 2:00
Marching Band 4:00
Fireworks 9:00

What time does each event begin?
Draw a line from each ticket booth to its event.

2:00

4:00

9:00

Matching Times with Events

Which instrument does each child play?
Find the stickers for page 7.
Place each sticker with the correct musician.

Matching

Find the stickers for page 8.
Place each hat sticker on the person who wears it.

Matching

Draw a line from each mother to her baby.

Matching

PRETTY PATTERNS

Color the flowers that come next in the patterns.
The first one is done for you.

Working with Patterns

Find the stickers for page 11.
Use the stickers to continue the patterns.

Working with Patterns

PERFECT PATTERNS

Find the stickers for page 12.
Use the stickers to continue the patterns.

Working with Patterns

Find the stickers for page 13. Say the names of the pictures.
Put each sticker with the letter that begins its name.

A

Trace **A**. Then write **A**.

B

Trace **B**. Then write **B**.

C

Trace **C**. Then write **C**.

D

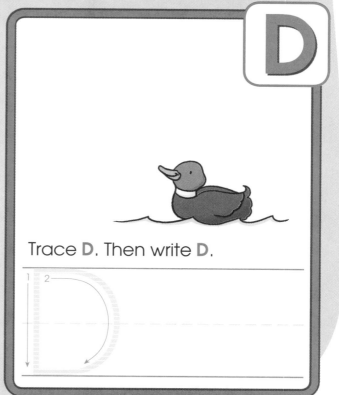

Trace **D**. Then write **D**.

Learning about the Letters A–D

Find the stickers for page 14. Say the names of the pictures.
Put each sticker with the letter that begins its name.

E

Trace E. Then write E.

F

Trace F. Then write F.

G

Trace G. Then write G.

H

Trace H. Then write H.

Find the stickers for page 15. Say the names of the pictures.
Put each sticker with the letter that begins its name.

I

Trace I. Then write I.

J

Trace J. Then write J.

K

Trace K. Then write K.

L

Trace L. Then write L.

Learning about the Letters I–L

Find the stickers for page 16. Say the names of the pictures.
Put each sticker with the letter that begins its name.

M

Trace **M**. Then write **M**.

N

Trace **N**. Then write **N**.

O

Trace **O**. Then write **O**.

P

Trace **P**. Then write **P**.

Learning about the Letters M-P

Find the stickers for page 17. Say the names of the pictures.
Put each sticker with the letter that begins its name.

Q

Trace **Q**. Then write **Q**.

R

Trace **R**. Then write **R**.

S

Trace **S**. Then write **S**.

T

Trace **T**. Then write **T**.

Learning about the Letters Q–T

Sticker & Crayon Page!

Find the stickers for page 18. Say the names of the pictures.
Put each sticker with the letter that begins its name.

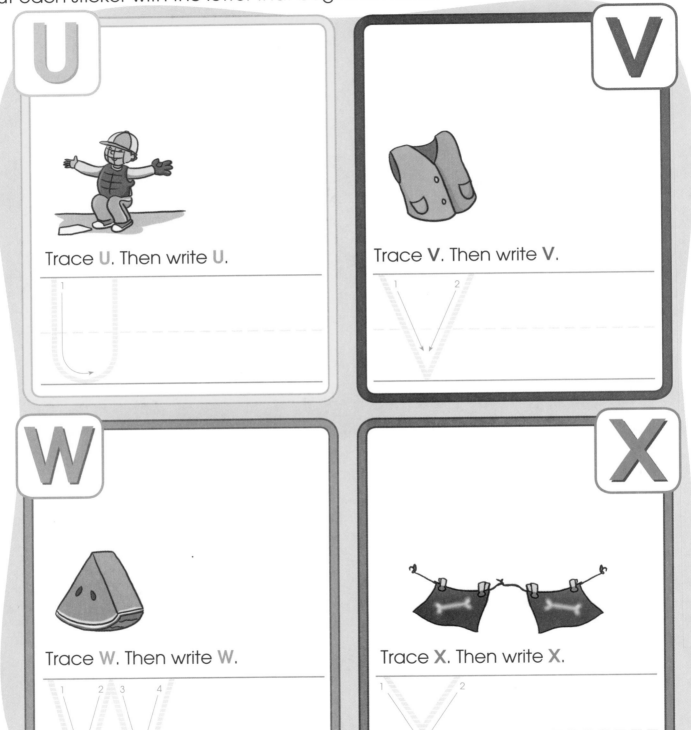

U

Trace **U**. Then write **U**.

V

Trace **V**. Then write **V**.

W

Trace **W**. Then write **W**.

X

Trace **X**. Then write **X**.

Find the stickers for page 19. Say the names of the pictures.
Put each sticker with the letter that begins its name.

Y

Trace **Y**. Then write **Y**.

Z

Trace **Z**. Then write **Z**.

Help **Y** find his friend **Z**.

Learning about the Letters Y & Z

Help put the toys away. Each toy goes in the bin marked with the letter that begins its name. Draw a line from each toy to the correct bin.

Working with Beginning Sounds

Find the stickers for page 21.
Follow each path, and place the sticker whose name begins with each letter.

Working with Beginning Sounds

ALL ABOARD!

Write the missing letters on the alphabet train.

A B C D E F G H I J K L M

Practicing Alphabetical Order
©School Zone Publishing Company

N O P Q R S T U V W X Y Z

Practicing Alphabetical Order

SEASIDE SHAPES

square   rectangle   triangle   circle

What is missing?
Trace the shapes to finish the scene.
Say the name of each shape as you trace it.

24

Learning about Shapes

Find the stickers for page 25. Use the stickers to fill in the missing shapes. Then finish coloring the picture.

Working with Shapes & Patterns

Color the ◺s **red**.

Color the ☐s **purple**.

Color the ◯s yellow.

Color the ▭s **green**.

Color the rest of the picture with your favorite colors.

Crayon Page!

Connect the dots from **1** to **10**. Color the picture.

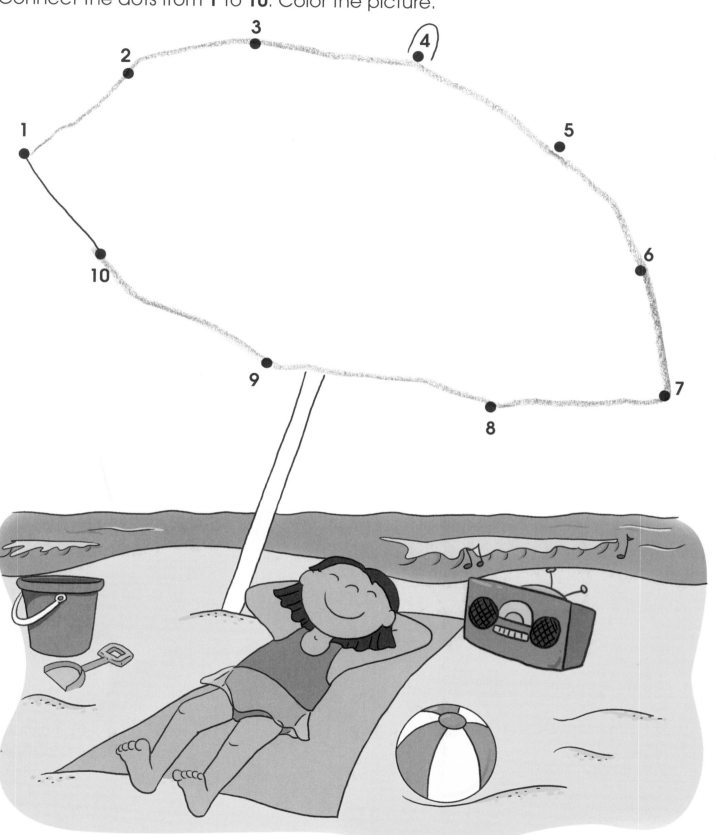

Practicing Number Sequencing

Count the balloons. Use the number stickers for page 28 to show how many balloons there are. Then color the balloons.

1 = orange

2 = red

3 = **purple**

4 = green

5 = blue

COUNTING EGGS

Crayon Page!

Draw a line from each bird to the nest that contains the correct number of eggs.

5 eggs

2 eggs

4 eggs

3 eggs

29

Counting; Matching Numbers to Objects

LOTS OF LEGS

 Sticker & Crayon Page!

Find the stickers for page 30. Count the number of legs each creature has, and place each creature in the correct scene.

4 legs

6 legs

2 legs

0 legs

Circle the number of legs the  has.

2 4 6 8

Counting; Matching Numbers to Objects

Use the graph to answer the questions.

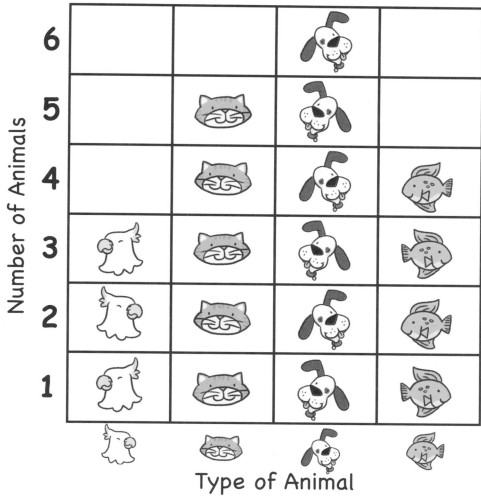

Type of Animal

How many 🐱s?

How many 🐶s?

How many 🐦s?

How many 🐟?

Working with Graphs

FUN AT THE AMUSEMENT PARK

Find the stickers for page 32.
Count the number of children on each ride.
Place each ride sticker under the correct part of the graph.

Number of Riders

8
7
6
5
4
3
2
1

Type of Ride

32

Counting & Graphing

©School Zone Publishing Company

Counting & Graphing

TONS OF TOYS

Crayon Page!

Count the toys. Then answer the questions.

How many s? _____

How many s? _____

How many s? _____

How many s? _____

34

Counting

©School Zone Publishing Company

DUCKS IN A ROW

Sticker Page!

Some ducks are missing numbers.
Use the stickers for page 35 to fill in the missing numbers.

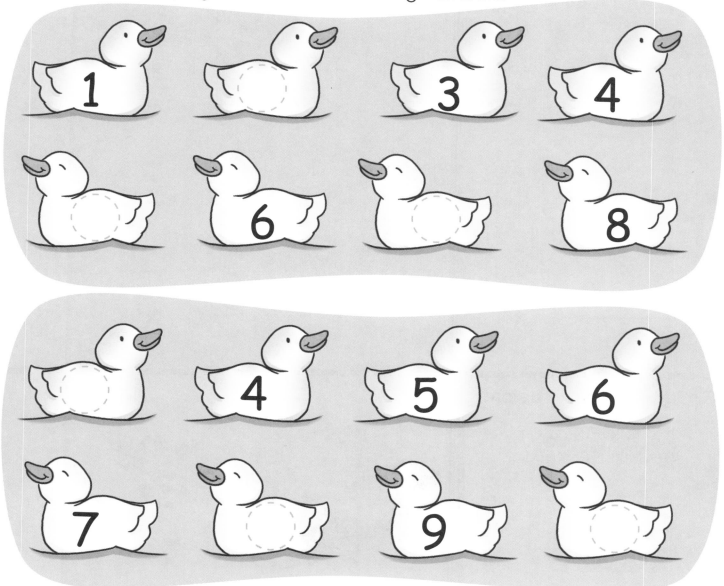

35

©School Zone Publishing Company

Practicing Number Sequencing

before   after

Write the number that comes **before** each set of numbers.

_____ 2 3   _____ 6 7

_____ 4 5   _____ 5 6

_____ 3 4   _____ 8 9

Circle what comes **before**.

Practicing Sequencing: Concept of *Before*   ©School Zone Publishing Company

before

after

Write the number that comes **after** each set of numbers.

4 5 _____   2 3 _____

6 7 _____   1 2 _____

5 6 _____   3 4 _____

Circle what comes **after**.

Practicing Sequencing: Concept of *After*

PERFECT PAIRS

Use the stickers for page 38 to turn each shoe into a pair.

Color the socks.

Matching; Making Pairs

Find the stickers for page 39.
Place each sticker with the correct group.

Classifying

Find the stickers for page 40.
Place each sticker with the correct group.

Classifying

©School Zone Publishing Company

Find the stickers for page 41.
Place each sticker with the correct group.

Classifying

DRIVING ALONG

Draw a line from each vehicle to the job it does.

42

Find the stickers for page 43.
Use the stickers to fill the fruit and vegetable stands.

Classifying

ANIMAL HABITATS

Find the stickers for page 44.
Place each animal in its home.

Matching

Draw a line from each animal to what it eats.

Matching

SEASONAL SPORTS

What can you do during the different seasons?
Add the stickers for page 46 to the scenes.

Learning about the Seasons

©School Zone Publishing Company

Circle what does not belong in the picture.

Circle what you might do after winter fun.

Separating What Belongs & Does Not Belong

Use the coin stickers for page 48 to show how much each item costs.

Count the pennies.
Write how many are in each group.

2

_____ ¢   _____ ¢   3 ¢   4 ¢

Matching & Counting Coins

Count the pennies.
Draw a line from each group of pennies to the item that costs the same amount.

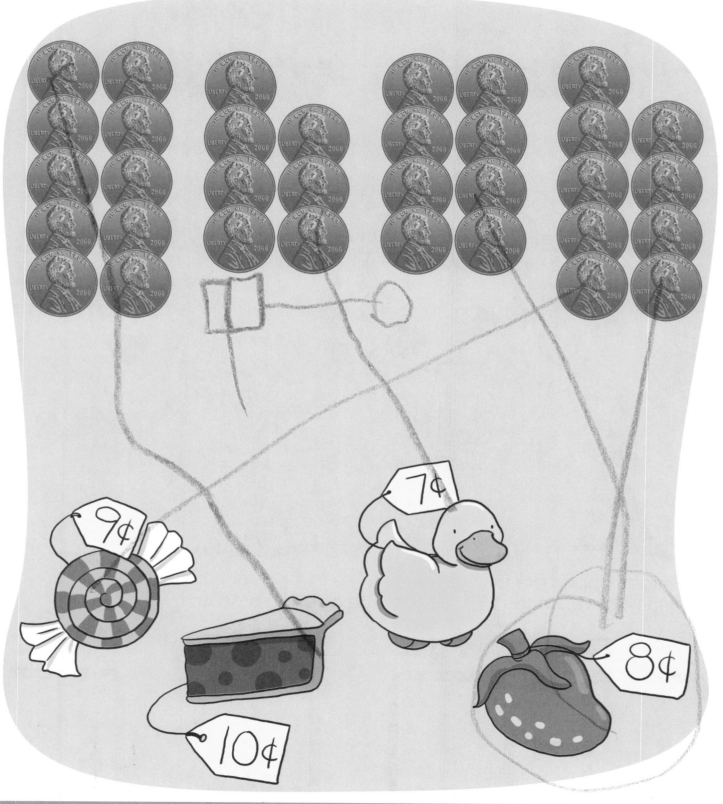

9¢

7¢

8¢

10¢

Counting Coins; Matching Amounts

Draw an apple on each tree.

How many apples are there now?
Write the answers in the boxes below the addition problems.

2+1=

3+1=

0+1=

1+1=

Adding

PLENTY OF PENNIES

 Crayon Page!

Count the pennies. Write the numbers in the boxes.

Write how many pennies there are in all.

 2 + 2 =

 2 + 3 =

Circle what you can buy with **5** pennies.

 Lollipops 5¢

 STICKERS 10¢

Counting & Adding Coins; Matching Amounts

Draw a line from each puzzle piece to the correct picture.

Draw the other half of each picture.

Matching; Visual Discrimination

ANIMAL OUTLINES

Sticker & Crayon Page!

goat   cow   cat   dog

Find the animal name stickers for page 53. Place each name on the outline with the matching shape. Draw a line from each name to that animal in the picture.

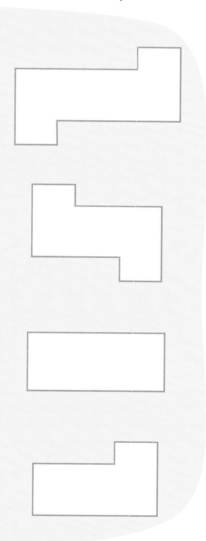

Draw an outline around each word.

great   job

Matching; Visual Discrimination

RHYME TIME

hat cat bat rat

Find the stickers for page 54.
Add one more rhyming word to each row.

cat bat

coat goat

bear chair

dog log

OODLES OF OPPOSITES

up   down

Draw lines to match the opposites.

sad

new

empty

hot

full

cold

happy

old

Circle the opposites.

Working with Opposites

Circle or to show how you would feel.

Learning about Emotions

Help pass out the picnic food. Use the stickers for page 57 to fill the plates.

wants a hot dog.

wants pizza.

wants a hamburger.

Matching; Reading Comprehension

Write **1** to show what happened **first**.
Write **2** to show what happened **next**.
Write **3** to show what happened **last**.

Sequencing/Story Order

Use the stickers for page 59 to finish the scene.

Help the rabbit get to her babies.

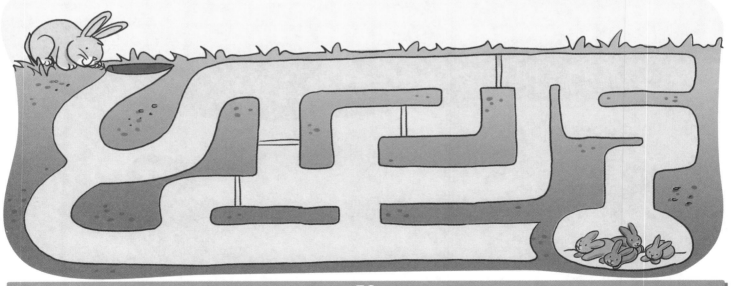

Visual Discrimination

Use the stickers for page 60 to finish the scene.

Circle what goes with s.

cat

dog

Use the stickers for page 61 to finish the scene.

Visual Discrimination

SPRINGTIME FUN

Sticker & Crayon Page!

Use the stickers for page 62 to finish the scene.

Draw what is missing.

Visual Discrimination

Use the stickers for page 63 to finish the scene.

Visual Discrimination

Use the stickers for page 64 to finish the scene.
Then color the hot air balloon.

Visual Discrimination

Color the red.

Use your to trace the word **red**.

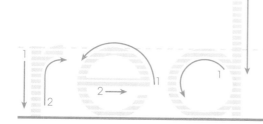

Color what is **red**.

Learning about the Color Red

VALENTINE RED

Color the ♡ red.

Learning about the Color Red

Circle **2** things that are **red**.

Learning about the Color Red

Color the orange.

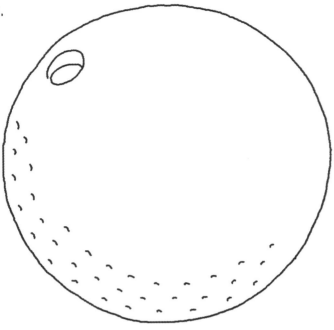

Use your to trace the word orange.

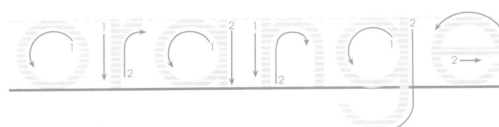

Color what is orange.

Learning about the Color Orange

Color the orange.

Learning about the Color Orange

Circle 2 things that are orange.

Color the 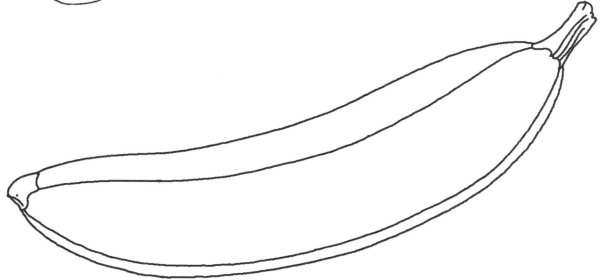 yellow.

Use your to trace the word yellow.

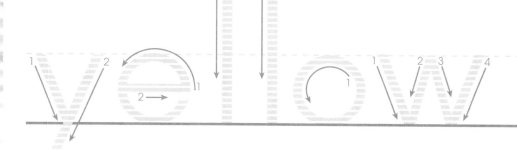

Color what is yellow.

Color the  yellow.

YELLOW THINGS

Circle 3 things that are yellow.

73

Color the green.

Use your ✏️ to trace the word **green**.

Color what is **green**.

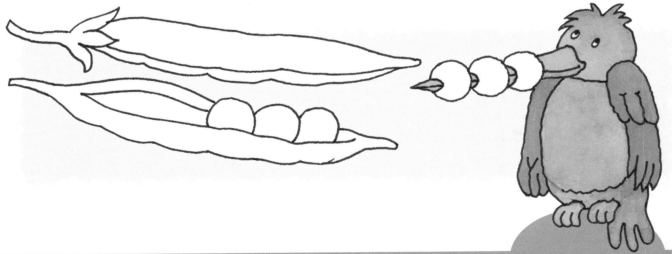

Learning about the Color Green

Color the green.

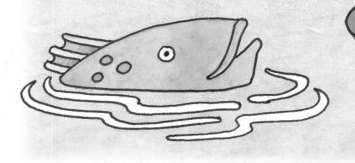

Learning about the Color Green

GREEN THINGS

Crayon Page!

Circle **3** things that are **green**.

76

Learning about the Color Green

©School Zone Publishing Company

Color the  blue.

Use your to trace the word **blue**.

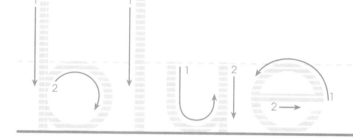

Color what is **blue**.

Learning about the Color Blue

MAIL CARRIER BLUE

Color the  blue.

Learning about the Color Blue

©School Zone Publishing Company

Circle 3 things that are blue.

Learning about the Color Blue

Color the  **purple**.

Use your ✏️ to trace the word **purple**.

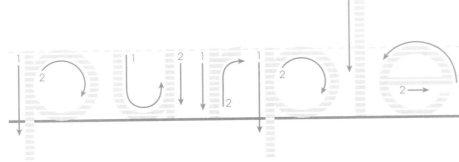

Color what is **purple**.

Learning about the Color Purple

Color the 🍠 purple.

Circle **3** things that are **purple**.

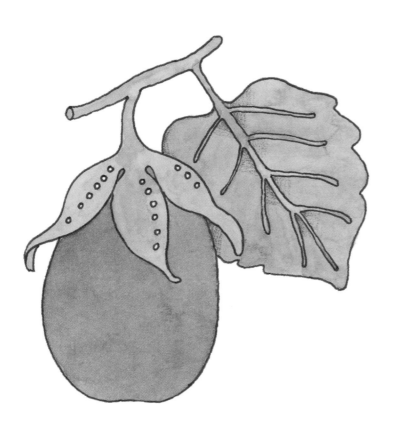

SQUIRREL BROWN

Color the  brown.

Use your  to trace the word **brown**.

brown

Color what is **brown**.

Learning about the Color Brown

BEAR BROWN

Color the  brown.

Learning about the Color Brown

Circle **2** things that are **brown**.

Learning about the Color Brown

Color the  black.

Use your to trace the word **black**.

Color what is **black**.

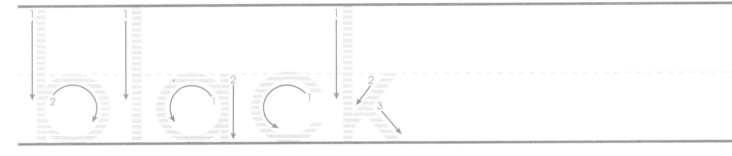

Color the s **black**.

Learning about the Color Black

BLACK THINGS

Circle **2** things that are **black**.

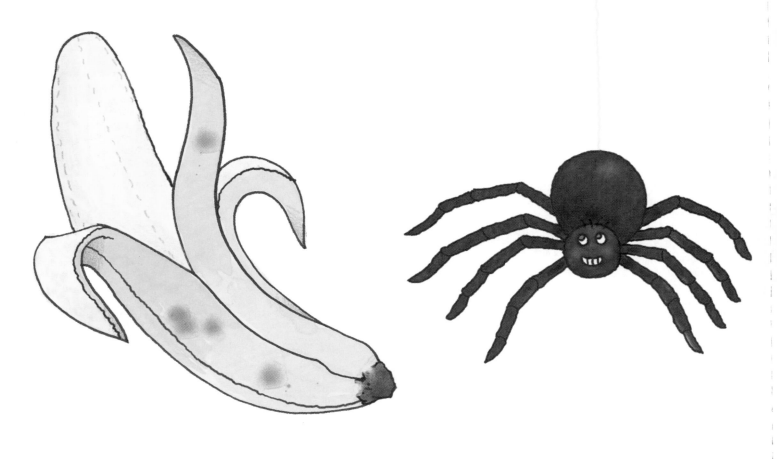

Learning about the Color Black

COLOR REVIEW

Draw a line from each crayon to the picture that is usually that color.
Color the pictures.

Reviewing Colors

Draw a line from each crayon to the picture that is usually that color.
Color the pictures.

Color the picture.

A = red   B = blue   C = brown   D = green

Reviewing Colors

Color the picture.

A = **blue**   B = **red**   C = **orange**   D = white

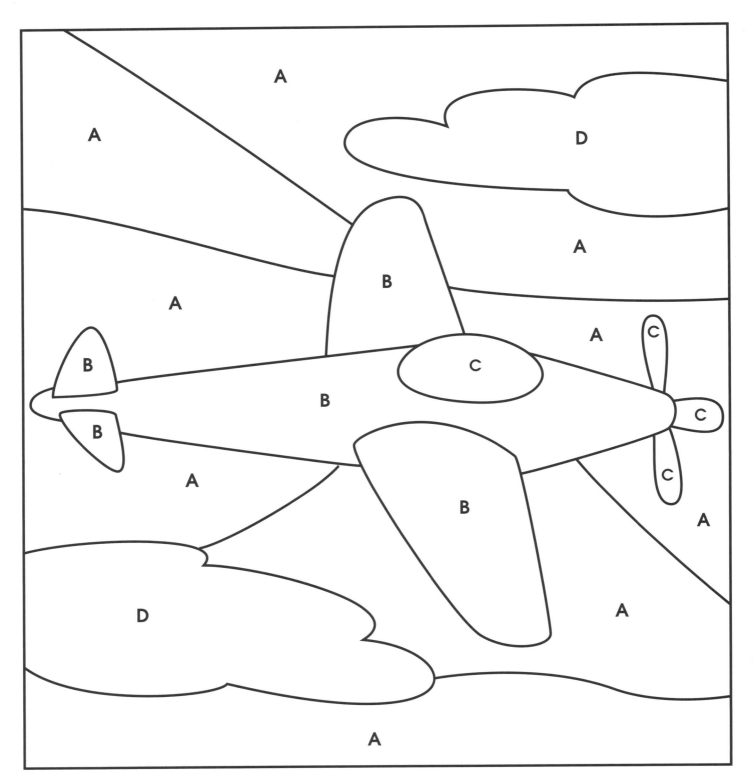

Reviewing Colors   ©School Zone Publishing Company

Color the picture.

A = **black** B = blue C = yellow D = green

Reviewing Colors

TERRIFIC TRUCK

Color the picture.

A = **purple**   B = white   C = **blue**
D = **brown**   E = **black**   F = **red**

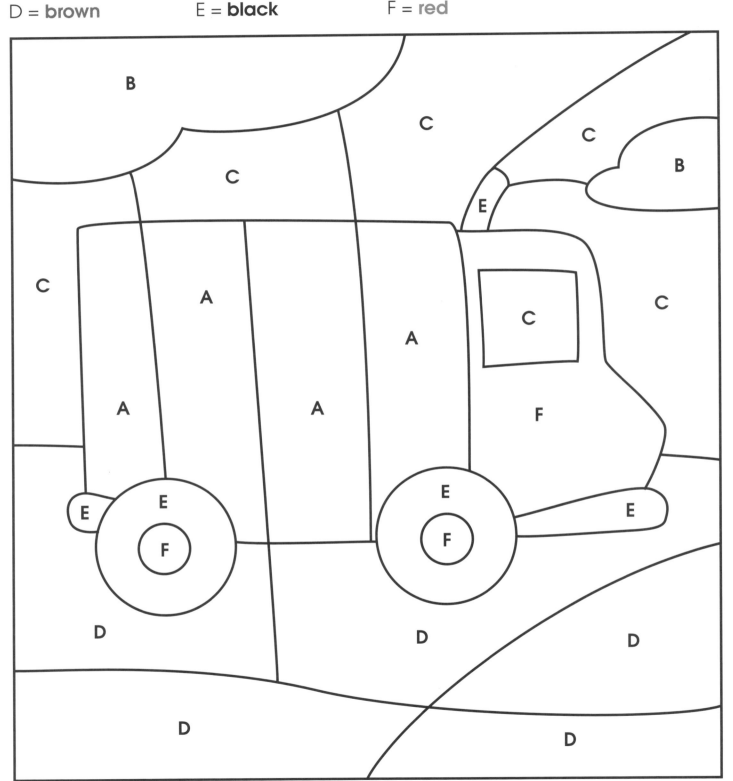

Reviewing Colors   ©School Zone Publishing Company

TASTY TREAT

Color the picture.

A = **brown**   B = **red**   C = **blue**

D = **purple**   E = green   F = yellow

Reviewing Colors

COLORS IN THE SKY

Color the picture.

A = **red**   B = **orange**   C = yellow   D = green

E = blue   F = **purple**   G = white

Reviewing Colors

Say the letters and the names of the pictures.

A B C D E

F G H I J

K L M N O

P Q R S T

U V W X Y Z

Learning the Letters of the Alphabet

THE LETTERS A-D

Find the stickers for page 98. Say the names of the pictures.
Put each sticker with the letter that begins its name.

A

B

C

D

Learning about the Letters A-D

Find the stickers for page 99. Add the stickers to the scene.

Learning about the Letters A–D

Find the stickers for page 100. Say the names of the pictures.
Put each sticker with the letter that begins its name.

E

F

G

H

Learning about the Letters E–H

©School Zone Publishing Company

Find the stickers for page 101. Add the stickers to the scene.

Learning about the Letters E–H

Find the stickers for page 102. Say the names of the pictures.
Put each sticker with the letter that begins its name.

Find the stickers for page 103. Add the stickers to the scene.

Learning about the Letters I–L

THE LETTERS M-P

Find the stickers for page 104. Say the names of the pictures.
Put each sticker with the letter that begins its name.

Learning about the Letters M-P

©School Zone Publishing Company

Find the stickers for page 105. Add the stickers to the scene.

Learning about the Letters M–P

Find the stickers for page 106. Say the names of the pictures.
Put each sticker with the letter that begins its name.

Learning about the Letters Q–T

Find the stickers for page 107. Add the stickers to the scene.

Learning about the Letters Q–T

Find the stickers for page 108. Say the names of the pictures.
Put each sticker with the letter that begins its name.

Find the stickers for page 109. Add the stickers to the scene.

Learning about the Letters U–X

Find the stickers for page 110. Say the names of the pictures.
Put each sticker with the letter that begins its name.

Y

Z

Connect the dots from **A** to **Z**. Color the picture.

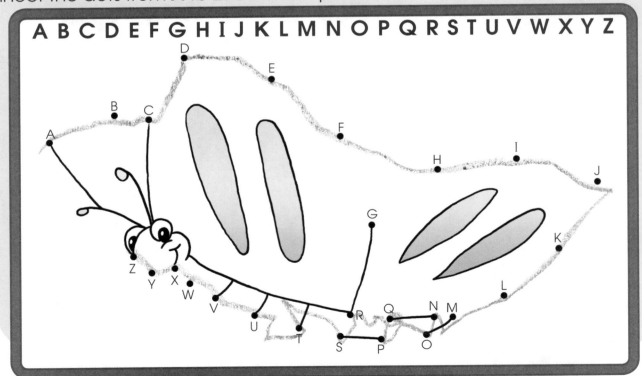

A B C D E F G H I J K L M N O P Q R S T U V W X Y Z

A TRIP TO THE ZOO

Find the stickers for page 111. Add the stickers to the scene.

Learning about the Letters Y & Z

A was an **ant**

Who seldom stood still,

Who made a nice house

In the side of a hill.

Practice tracing and writing the letter **A**.

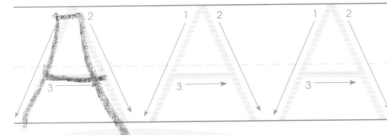

Letter Maze

Draw a line through all the **A** letters to get to the finish.

Start

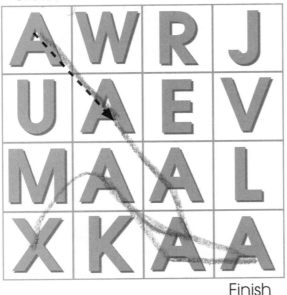

Finish

Tic-Tac-Toe

Connect the letter **A** and the pictures whose names start with **A**.

Learning about the Letter A

BARRY BAT

B was a **bat**

With an arm in a sling;

He flew 'round in circles

With only one wing.

Practice tracing and writing the letter **B**.

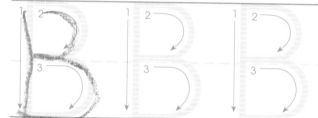

Letter Maze

Draw a line through all the **B** letters to get to the finish.

Start

O	B	N	P
M	B	B	R
Q	E	B	U
B	B	B	P

Finish

Tic-Tac-Toe

Connect the letter **B** and the pictures whose names start with **B**.

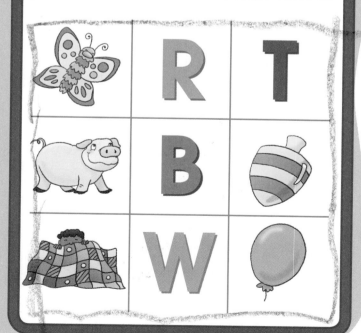

113

©School Zone Publishing Company

Learning about the Letter B

was a **camel**

Whose hump was misplaced;

When it was found,

He fixed it with paste.

Practice tracing and writing the letter **C**.

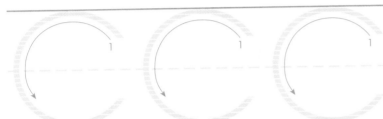

Letter Maze

Draw a line through all the **C** letters to get to the finish.

Start

V	B	I	C
F	N	G	C
C	C	C	C
C	K	T	R

Finish

Tic-Tac-Toe

Connect the letter **C** and the pictures whose names start with **C**.

Learning about the Letter C

 was a **dancer**

Who danced all day long;

When doing a two-step,

She'd burst into song.

Practice tracing and writing the letter **D**.

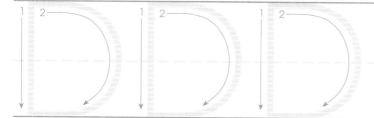

Letter Maze

Draw a line through all the **D** letters to get to the finish.

Start

D	K	M	B
D	D	D	D
X	P	G	D
R	Q	B	D

Finish

Tic-Tac-Toe

Connect the letter **D** and the pictures whose names start with **D**.

Learning about the Letter D

ELLIE EGG

Crayon Page!

E was an **egg**

Our feisty hen laid;

When she was done,

She asked to be paid.

Practice tracing and writing the letter E.

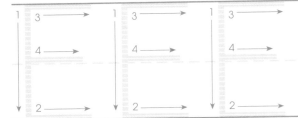

Letter Maze

Draw a line through all the E letters to get to the finish.

Start

X	F	E	E
U	A	E	G
E	E	E	B
E	Z	X	K

Finish

Tic-Tac-Toe

Connect the letter E and the pictures whose names start with E.

116

Learning about the Letter E

©School Zone Publishing Company

 was an **fox**

Who was clever and sly;

He crept into the kitchen

To eat cherry pie.

Practice tracing and writing the letter **F**.

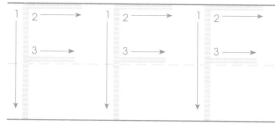

Letter Maze

Draw a line through all the **F** letters to get to the finish.

Start

E	F	R	E
E	F	F	M
M	C	F	P
J	W	F	F

Finish

Tic-Tac-Toe

Connect the letter **F** and the pictures whose names start with **F**.

Learning about the Letter F

GAVIN GANDER

 was a **gander**

With fuzzy, white down;

He dressed like a man

When he went into town.

Practice tracing and writing the letter G.

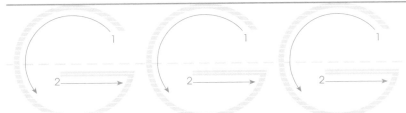

Letter Maze

Draw a line through all the **G** letters to get to the finish.

Start

N	G	C	Y
G	G	D	T
G	S	B	X
G	G	G	G

Finish

Tic-Tac-Toe

Connect the letter **G** and the pictures whose names start with **G**.

was a **heron**

Who stood in a stream;

The length of his neck

And his legs was extreme.

Practice tracing and writing the letter **H**.

Letter Maze

Draw a line through all the **H** letters to get to the finish.

Start

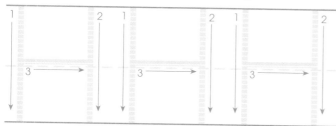

H	T	S	B
H	H	H	G
R	Z	H	F
H	H	H	Q

Finish

Tic-Tac-Toe

Connect the letter **H** and the pictures whose names start with **H**.

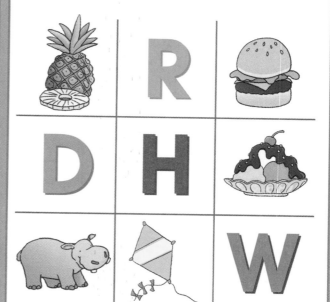

Learning about the Letter H

I was an **itch**

That bothered a bear;

He scratched and he scratched

'Til he lost all his hair.

Practice tracing and writing the letter I.

2 → 2 → 2 →
1 1 1
3 → 3 → 3 →

Letter Maze

Draw a line through all the
I letters to get to the finish.

Start

I	I	M	H
X	I	I	W
T	S	I	I
O	A	Z	I

Finish

Tic-Tac-Toe

Connect the letter I and the
pictures whose names start with I.

Learning about the Letter I

J was a **jogger**

Who tried not to stop;

Around and around

He went in one spot.

Practice tracing and writing the letter J.

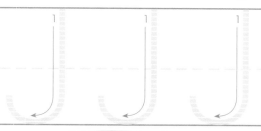

Letter Maze

Draw a line through all the J letters to get to the finish.

Start

Y	M	J	J
J	J	J	I
J	R	S	T
J	D	F	G

Finish

Tic-Tac-Toe

Connect the letter J and the pictures whose names start with J.

Learning about the Letter J

 was a **kitten**

Who lived on a farm;

She saw her black shadow,

Then ran to the barn.

Practice tracing and writing the letter K.

Letter Maze

Draw a line through all the K letters to get to the finish.

Start

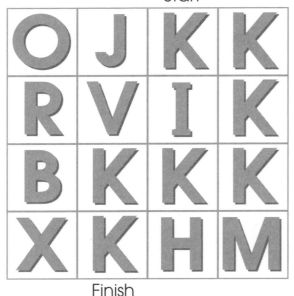

Finish

Tic-Tac-Toe

Connect the letter K and the pictures whose names start with K.

Learning about the Letter K

©School Zone Publishing Company

LARRY LLAMA

 was a **llama**

Who had his own house;

He rented two rooms

To a frog and a mouse.

Practice tracing and writing the letter L.

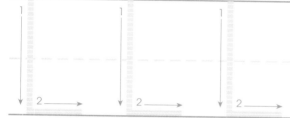

Letter Maze

Draw a line through all the L letters to get to the finish.

Start

T	L	P	O
M	L	L	L
Q	F	J	L
Z	R	C	L

Finish

Tic-Tac-Toe

Connect the letter L and the pictures whose names start with L.

Learning about the Letter L

M was a **mouse**

Who was digging a hole;

He was looking for diamonds,

But found only coal.

Practice tracing and writing the letter **M**.

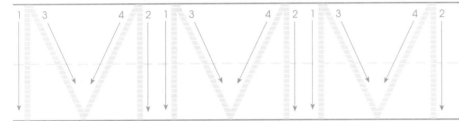

Letter Maze

Draw a line through all the **M** letters to get to the finish.

Start

M	W	R	K
M	I	N	V
M	M	M	L
C	D	M	A

Finish

Tic-Tac-Toe

Connect the letter **M** and the pictures whose names start with **M**.

N was a **narwhal**

Whose tooth did not gleam;

He went to the dentist,

Who polished it clean.

Practice tracing and writing the letter **N**.

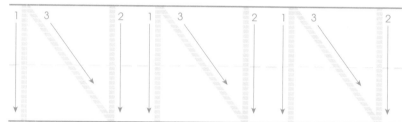

Letter Maze

Draw a line through all the
N letters to get to the finish.

Start

Y	C	M	N
R	N	N	N
T	N	M	Z
N	N	Z	P

Finish

Tic-Tac-Toe

Connect the letter **N** and the
pictures whose names start with **N**.

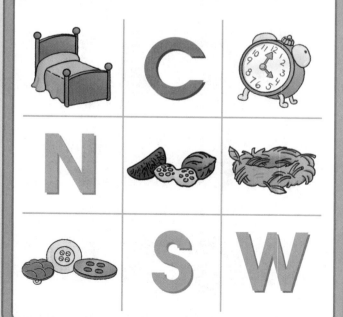

Learning about the Letter N

OWEN OTTER

 was an **otter**,

His wife was a loon;

They ate all their dinners

By the light of the moon.

Practice tracing and writing the letter O.

Letter Maze

Draw a line through all the O letters to get to the finish.

Start

C	O	O	Y
E	Q	O	M
K	X	O	O
S	G	B	O

Finish

Tic-Tac-Toe

Connect the letter O and the pictures whose names start with O.

PATTY PARROT

 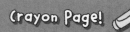

P

was a **parrot**

Who talked all day long;

But she couldn't say "Polly,"

She got it all wrong.

P-P-P

Paulee

Pally

squawk!

Practice tracing and writing the letter **P**.

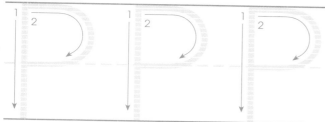

Letter Maze

Draw a line through all the **P** letters to get to the finish.

Start

D	P	R	I
N	P	P	O
Q	B	P	R
P	P	P	C

Finish

Tic-Tac-Toe

Connect the letter **P** and the pictures whose names start with **P**.

Z		
V	P	H

Learning about the Letter P

was a **quail**

Who lived in a tree;

She made tiny cookies

When friends came to tea.

Practice tracing and writing the letter **Q**.

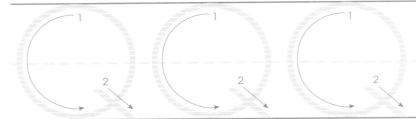

Letter Maze

Draw a line through all the **Q** letters to get to the finish.

Start

U	Q	P	G
X	Q	Q	O
H	C	Q	C
Q	Q	Q	Z

Finish

Tic-Tac-Toe

Connect the letter **Q** and the pictures whose names start with **Q**.

Learning about the Letter Q

 was a **raven**

Who lived in a tree;

He sat on a branch

And watched the TV.

Practice tracing and writing the letter **R**.

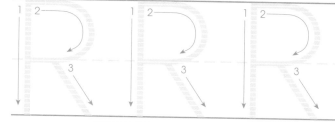

Letter Maze

Draw a line through all the **R** letters to get to the finish.

Start

J	Q	R	L
D	R	R	P
T	R	K	C
N	R	R	R

Finish

Tic-Tac-Toe

Connect the letter **R** and the pictures whose names start with **R**.

Learning about the Letter R

SIMON STORK

S was a **stork**

With a very long bill,

Who swallowed down fishes

And frogs to his fill.

Practice tracing and writing the letter S.

Letter Maze

Draw a line through all the S letters to get to the finish.

Start

D	H	R	S
M	S	S	S
J	S	I	C
S	S	L	E

Finish

Tic-Tac-Toe

Connect the letter S and the pictures whose names start with S.

Learning about the Letter S

 was a **toad**

Who forgot how to hop;

He took hopping lessons,

And now he can't stop.

Practice tracing and writing the letter T.

Letter Maze

Draw a line through all the
T letters to get to the finish.

Start

O	T	T	E
E	F	T	G
Q	L	T	P
J	I	T	T

Finish

Tic-Tac-Toe

Connect the letter T and the
pictures whose names start with T.

Learning about the Letter T

was my **uncle**

Who never sat down;

He slept standing up

In a flannel nightgown.

Practice tracing and writing the letter U.

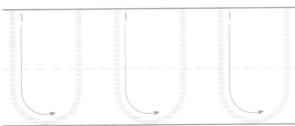

Letter Maze

Draw a line through all the U letters to get to the finish.

Start

O	V	U	U
V	W	V	U
U	U	U	U
U	R	H	E

Finish

Tic-Tac-Toe

Connect the letter U and the pictures whose names start with U.

Learning about the Letter U

 was a **violet**

In love with a rose;

When they went out to dinner,

She wore her best clothes.

Practice tracing and writing the letter V.

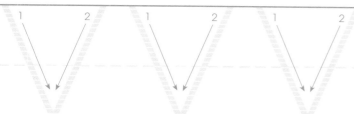

Letter Maze

Draw a line through all the V letters to get to the finish.

Start

V	V	W	O
Y	V	V	S
G	K	V	V
P	X	J	V

Finish

Tic-Tac-Toe

Connect the letter V and the pictures whose names start with V.

Learning about the Letter V

W was a **worm**

Who ate mud and dirt;

He chomped on a rock

That made his jaw hurt.

Practice tracing and writing the letter **W**.

Letter Maze

Draw a line through all the **W** letters to get to the finish.

Start

D	W	W	O
U	W	S	G
J	W	W	I
Y	Z	W	K

Finish

Tic-Tac-Toe

Connect the letter **W** and the pictures whose names start with **W**.

marks the spot

On an old treasure map;

If you don't find the gold,

You'll fall in a trap.

Practice tracing and writing the letter X.

Letter Maze

Draw a line through all the X letters to get to the finish.

Start

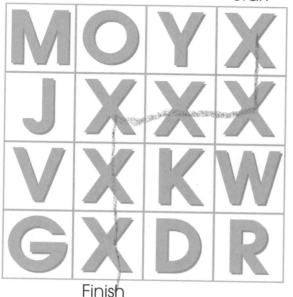

M	O	Y	X
J	X	X	X
V	X	K	W
G	X	D	R

Finish

Tic-Tac-Toe

Connect the letter X and the pictures whose names start with X.

135

 **Y** was a **yak**

From the land of Tibet;

Lonesome for home,

He took off in a jet.

Practice tracing and writing the letter **Y**.

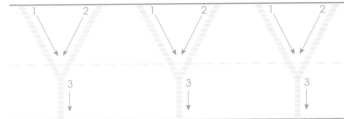

Letter Maze

Draw a line through all the **Y** letters to get to the finish.

Start

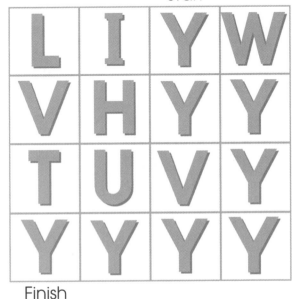

Finish

Tic-Tac-Toe

Connect the letter **Y** and the pictures whose names start with **Y**.

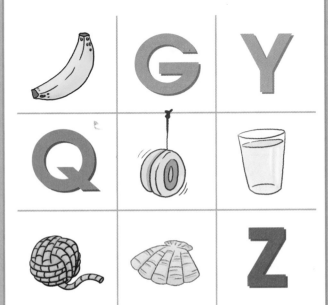

Learning about the Letter Y

Z

Z was a **zebra**

Who bought many socks;

He carried them home

In a large, yellow box.

Practice tracing and writing the letter Z.

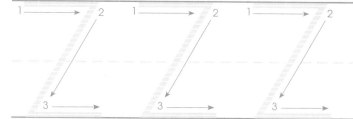

Letter Maze

Draw a line through all the Z letters to get to the finish.

Start

Z	Z	P	R
Y	Z	N	E
K	Z	M	H
D	Z	Z	Z

Finish

Tic-Tac-Toe

Connect the letter Z and the pictures whose names start with Z.

T		E
	F	
	Z	

Learning about the Letter Z

Crayon Page!

Draw a line from each picture to the letter that begins its name.

M
B
I
H
Z
P

Crayon Page!

Draw a line from each picture to the letter that begins its name.

Matching Pictures to Beginning Sounds

BEGINNING SOUNDS REVIEW

Draw a line from each picture to the letter that begins its name.

C

D

X

S

F

O

BEGINNING SOUNDS REVIEW

Draw a line from each picture to the letter that begins its name.

G
Y
R
W
K
T
J

Matching Pictures to Beginning Sounds

FOLLOW THE ALPHABET TRAIL!

Help fill in the missing pictures using the stickers for pages 142 and 143.

©School Zone Publishing Company

Practicing Alphabetical Order

LOOKING AROUND THE CITY

Find the stickers for pages 144 and 145. Place each sticker in the correct box. Circle the pictures in the scene.

| Airplane | Flag | Whale | Iguana |

Relating Words to Pictures; Finding Hidden Pictures

| Monkey | Juggler | Van | Bike |

Relating Words to Pictures; Finding Hidden Pictures

DOWN ON THE FARM

Find the stickers for pages 146 and 147. Place each sticker in the correct box.
Circle the pictures in the scene.

Goat

Cow

Tractor

Pig

Relating Words to Pictures; Finding Hidden Pictures

©School Zone Publishing Company

Farmer

Horse

Quilt

Dog

147

Relating Words to Pictures; Finding Hidden Pictures

OUT ON THE WATER

Find the stickers for pages 148 and 149. Place each sticker in the correct box.
Circle the pictures in the scene.

Walrus

Pelican

Crab

Elephant

Relating Words to Pictures; Finding Hidden Pictures

Octopus	Robot	Starfish	Girl

Relating Words to Pictures; Finding Hidden Pictures

FUN IN THE PARK

Find the stickers for pages 150 and 151. Place each sticker in the correct box. Circle the pictures in the scene.

Bird	Wagon	Kite	Net

Relating Words to Pictures; Finding Hidden Pictures

Umbrella	Duck	Squirrel	Ladder

Relating Words to Pictures; Finding Hidden Pictures

Find the stickers for page 152. Match the stickers to the words.
Say each pair of rhyming words.

hats

cats

frogs

dogs

cakes

snakes

Matching Pictures to Words; Rhyming Words

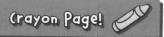

Connect the dots from **A** to **Z**.
Color the picture.

A B C D E F G H I J K L M N O P Q R S T U V W X Y Z

Practicing Alphabetical Order

Connect the dots from **A** to **Z**.
Color the picture.

A B C D E F G H I J K L M N O P Q R S T U V W X Y Z

Practicing Alphabetical Order

PLAYGROUND PAL

Connect the dots from **A** to **Z**.
Color the picture.

A B C D E F G H I J K L M N O P Q R S T U V W X Y Z

Practicing Alphabetical Order

FOREST FRIEND

Connect the dots from **A** to **Z**.
Color the picture.

A B C D E F G H I J K L M N O P Q R S T U V W X Y Z

Practicing Alphabetical Order

MOUNTAIN CLIMBER

Connect the dots from **A** to **Z**.
Color the picture.

A B C D E F G H I J K L M N O P Q R S T U V W X Y Z

Practicing Alphabetical Order

Connect the dots from **A** to **Z**.
Color the picture.

A B C D E F G H I J K L M N O P Q R S T U V W X Y Z

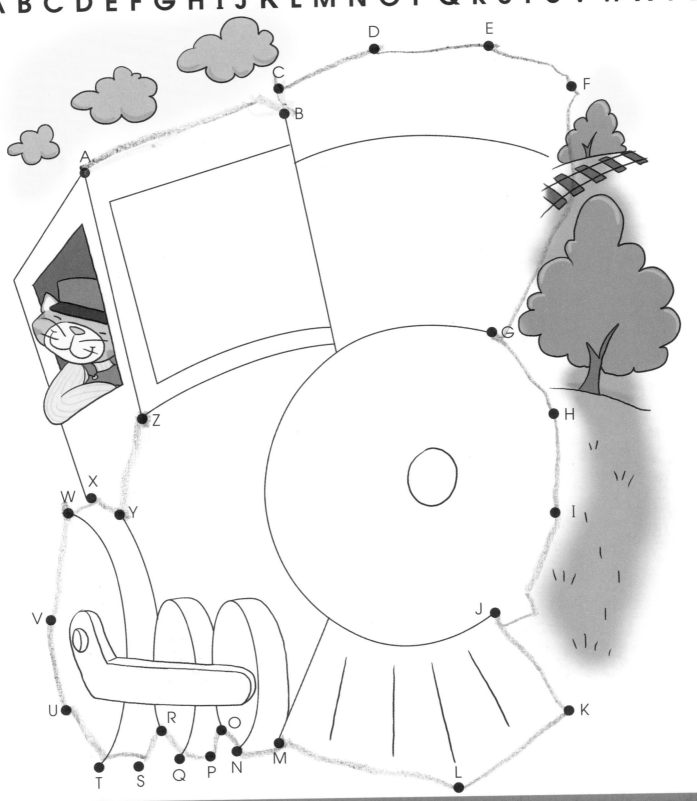

WAKE-UP CALL

 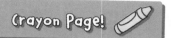

Connect the dots from **A** to **Z**.
Color the picture.

A B C D E F G H I J K L M N O P Q R S T U V W X Y Z

©School Zone Publishing Company

Practicing Alphabetical Order

Connect the dots from **A** to **Z**.
Color the picture.

A B C D E F G H I J K L M N O P Q R S T U V W X Y Z

Practicing Alphabetical Order

PARTY SQUARES

This ☐ is a **square**.
Trace the ☐s.

Learning about Squares

ROBOTIC SQUARES

Color the ☐ s **red**.

Coloring Squares

©School Zone Publishing Company

Color the ☐ s **purple**.

Make the shape a ☐. Then draw a ☐.

Coloring & Drawing Squares

SQUARE ART

Color the areas marked with a ▢ green.

Finding & Coloring Squares

LOOKING FOR SQUARES

 and count the ☐ shapes in the picture.

Finding & Counting Squares

SEEING CIRCLES

This ◯ is a **circle**.
Trace the ◯s.

166

Learning about Circles

Color the ◯s yellow.

Coloring Circles

Color the ⬤s green.

Make the shape a ⬤. Then draw a ⬤.

Coloring & Drawing Circles

CIRCLE ART

Color the areas marked with a orange.

Finding & Coloring Circles

LOOKING FOR CIRCLES

✓ and count the ◯ shapes in the picture.

Finding & Counting Circles

TENT TRIANGLES

This △ is a **triangle**.
Trace the △s.

Learning about Triangles

Color the △s **purple**.

Coloring Triangles

Color the △s orange.

Make the shape a △. Then draw a △.

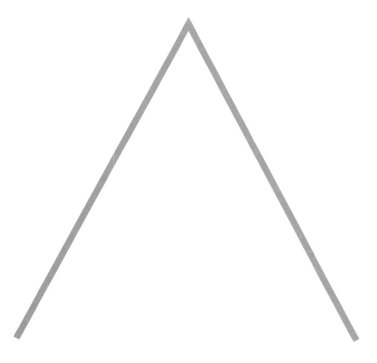

Coloring & Drawing Triangles

TRIANGLE ART

Color the areas marked with a △ blue.

Finding & Coloring Triangles

LOOKING FOR TRIANGLES

Crayon Page!

✔ and count the △ shapes in the picture.

175

©School Zone Publishing Company

Finding & Counting Triangles

SEEING RECTANGLES

This ▭ is a **rectangle**.

Trace the ▭ s.

Learning about Rectangles

Color the ▭ s red.

Coloring Rectangles

Crayon Page!

Color the ▯s **blue**.

Make the shape a ▯. Then draw a ▯.

Coloring & Drawing Rectangles

RECTANGLE ART

Color the areas marked with a ☐ green.

Finding & Coloring Rectangles

✓ and count the ☐ shapes in the picture.

Finding & Counting Rectangles

©School Zone Publishing Company

OVAL EGGS

This ⬭ is an oval.
Trace the ⬭s.

Learning about Ovals

OVALS THAT FLY

Color the ⬭s **purple**.

Coloring Ovals

Color the ⬭s green.

Make the shape an ⬭. Then draw an ⬭.

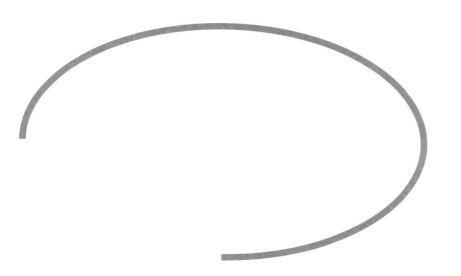

Coloring & Drawing Ovals

Color the areas marked with an ⬭ **red**.

Finding & Coloring Ovals

LOOKING FOR OVALS

 and count the ⬭ shapes in the picture.

Finding & Counting Ovals

Draw lines to match the shapes.

Matching Shapes

A BLAST OF SHAPES

Color the picture.

⬭ = **purple**   ▢ = blue   △ = green   ◯ = yellow   ▭ = orange

Finding & Coloring Shapes

SHAPES SEEN WHILE SAILING

Color all the ◯s yellow.

Color all the ▢s blue.

Finding & Coloring Shapes

Color all the △s **purple**.

Color all the ▭s **red**.

Finding & Coloring Shapes

SHAPE SURPRISE

Crayon Page!

Color the picture.

◯ = **purple** ▢ = blue △ = green ◯ = yellow ▢ = orange

Finding & Coloring Shapes   ©School Zone Publishing Company

SPRINGTIME SHAPES

Crayon Page!

Follow this pattern ⬭ ◻ ⬭ ◻ ⬭ ◻ to help the bear get to the picnic.

Following Patterns of Shapes

SWIMMING SHAPES

Follow this pattern   to help Mia get out of the pool.

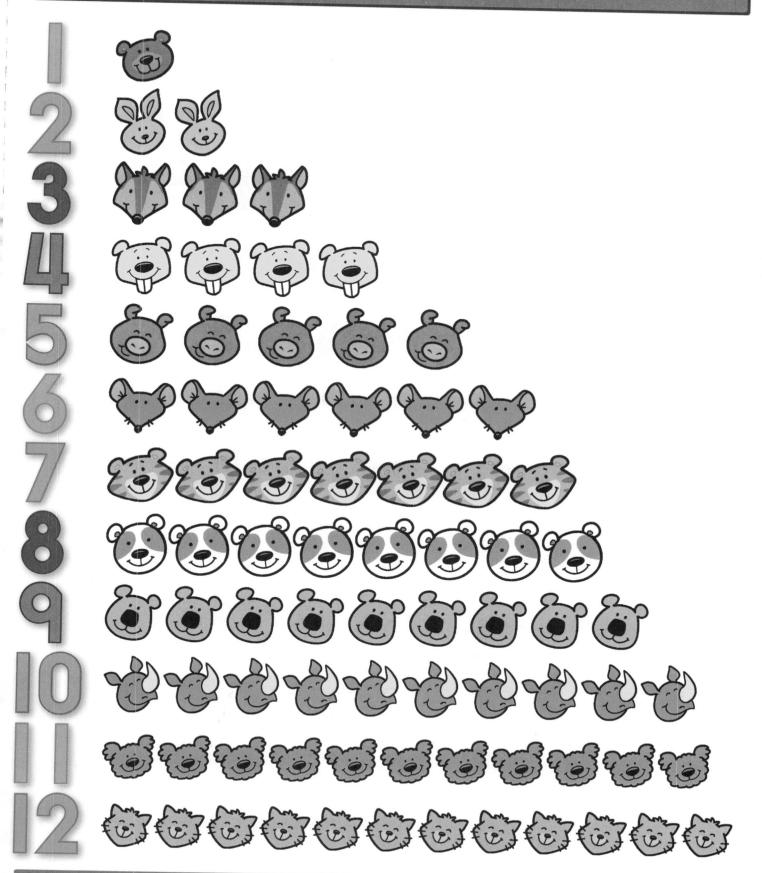

Learning the Numbers 1–12

1
One

Practice tracing and writing the number 1.

Place 1 ⭐ sticker.

Learning about the Number 1

©School Zone Publishing Company

Circle 1 🕊.

Color 1 🐘.

Add 1 🎈 sticker to the scene.

　　　　　Learning about the Number 1

Practice tracing and writing the number 2.

2 2

Place 2  stickers.

Circle **2** s.

Color **2** s.

Add **2**  stickers to the scene.

Learning about the Number 2

3
Three

Practice tracing and writing the number **3**.

3 3

Place **3** ⭐ stickers.

Learning about the Number 3

©School Zone Publishing Company

Circle **3** s.

Color **3** s.

Add **3** stickers to the scene.

Learning about the Number 3

LAZY LIZARDS

4 Four

Practice tracing and writing the number 4.

Place 4 ⭐ stickers.

Learning about the Number 4

Circle 4 🐍 s.

Color 4 🦎 s.

Add 4 🐢 stickers to the scene.

Learning about the Number 4

5
Five

Practice tracing and writing the number **5**.

5 5

Place **5** 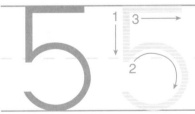 stickers.

Learning about the Number 5

Circle 5 🌳s.

Color 5 🦩s.

Add 5 🐟 stickers to the scene.

Learning about the Number 5

6 Six

Practice tracing and writing the number 6.

6 6

Place 6 ⭐ stickers.

Learning about the Number 6

Circle 6 🍎s.

Color 6 🌼s.

Add 3 🐿 stickers to make a group of 6 🐿s.

Learning about the Number 6

7
Seven

Practice tracing and writing the number 7.

7

Place 7  stickers.

Learning about the Number 7

©School Zone Publishing Company

Circle 7 s.

Color 7 s.

Add 5 stickers to make a group of 7 s.

Learning about the Number 7

8
Eight

Practice tracing and writing the number **8**.

Place **8**  stickers.

Circle **8** ducks.

Color **8** rabbits.

Add **4** chick stickers to make a group of **8** chicks.

Learning about the Number 8

9
Nine

Practice tracing and writing the number 9.

Place 9  stickers.

Learning about the Number 9

Circle 9 🎩 s.

Color 9 🧢 s.

Add 3 🧸 stickers to make a group of 9 🧸 s.

Learning about the Number 9

10
Ten

Practice tracing and writing the number 10.

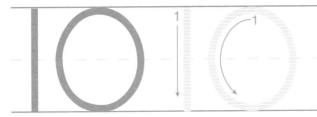

Place 10 ⭐ stickers.

Learning about the Number 10

Circle 10 🌼s.

Color 10 🍄s.

Add 4 🦋 stickers to make a group of 10 🦋s.

Learning about the Number 10

11
Eleven

Practice tracing and writing the number 11.

Place 11 ⭐ stickers.

Circle **11** s.

Color **11** s.

Add **3** stickers to make a group of **11** s.

Learning about the Number 11

Practice tracing and writing the number 12.

Place 12  stickers.

Learning about the Number 12

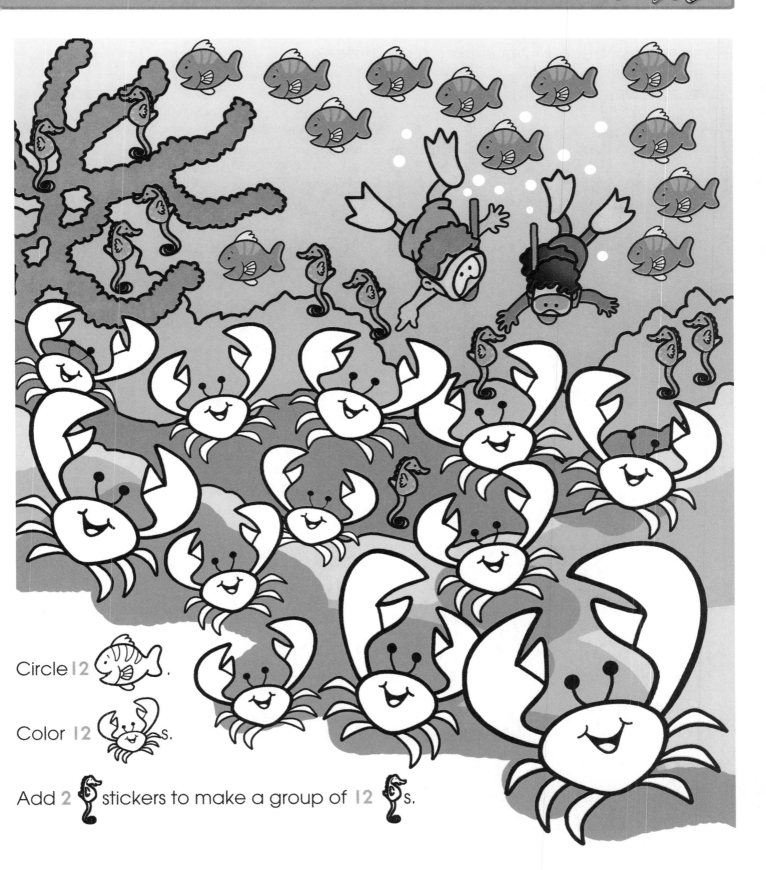

Circle 12 🐠.

Color 12 🦀s.

Add 2 🌿 stickers to make a group of 12 🌿s.

Learning about the Number 12

SEEN ON SAFARI

Count the animals in each set.
Place the correct number sticker in each box.

Reviewing the Numbers 1–4

©School Zone Publishing Company

Read each number.
Circle the correct number of animals in each row.

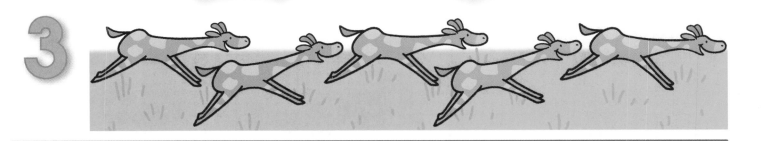

Reviewing the Numbers 1–4

FEATHERED FRIENDS

Count the birds in each set.
Place the correct number sticker in each box.

Reviewing the Numbers 5–8

©School Zone Publishing Company

Read each number.
Circle the correct number of birds in each row.

Reviewing the Numbers 5–8

FLYING HIGH

Count the objects in each set.
Place the correct number sticker in each box.

Reviewing the Numbers 9–12

Read each number.
Circle the correct number of objects in each row.

9
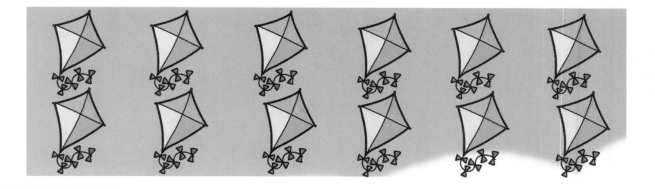

10

11

12
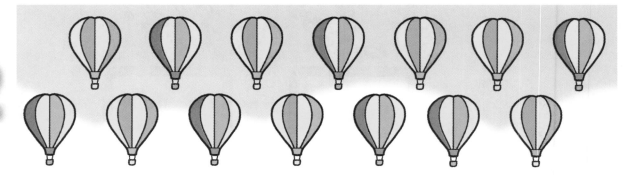

Reviewing the Numbers 9–12

SNACK TIME

Write the missing numbers and add the missing picture stickers to show the numbers from 1 to 12.

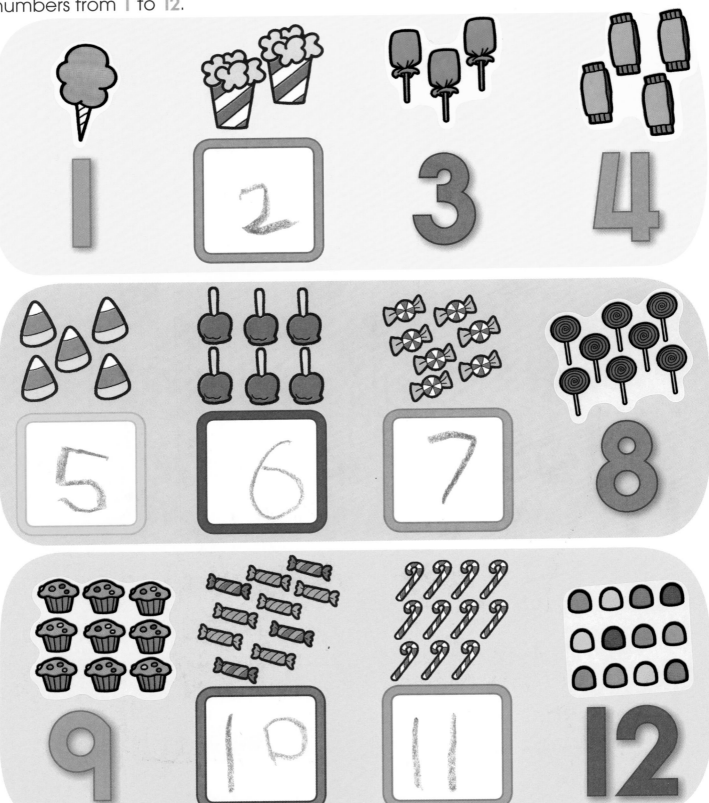

Reviewing the Numbers 1-12

SWEET SURPRISE

Connect the dots from 1 to 12.
Color the picture.

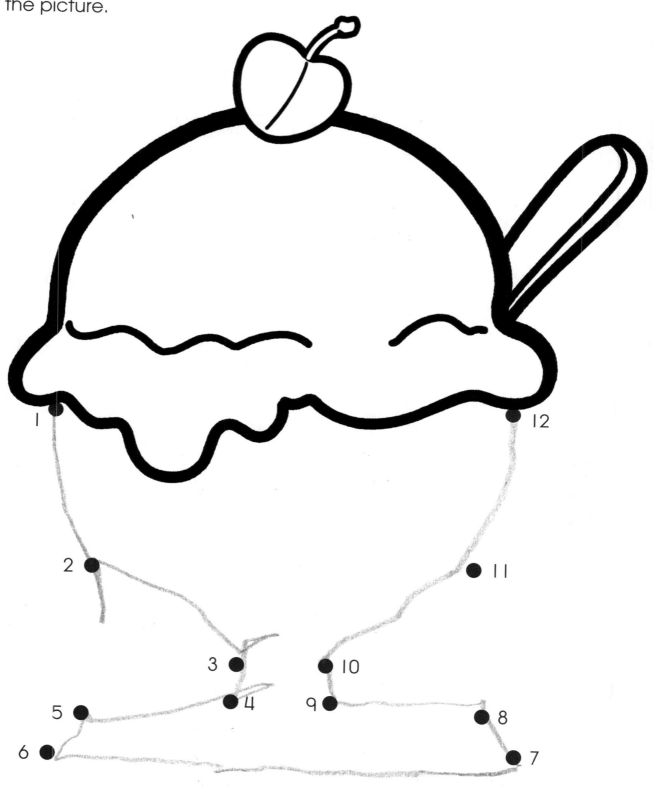

Reviewing Numerical Order

COLORFUL CLOWN

Crayon Page!

Color the **1** red.
Color the **2**s orange.
Color the **3**s yellow.
Color the **4**s green.
Color the **5**s blue.
Color the **6**s purple.
Color the **7**s brown.
Color the **8**s black.
Leave the **9**s white.
Give the **10**s black spots.
Give the **11**s brown spots.
Give the **12**s black stripes.

226

Reviewing the Numbers 1–12

©School Zone Publishing Company

Crayon Page!

Connect the dots from **1** to **12**.
Color the picture.

Reviewing Numerical Order

IN GOOD COMPANY

Count each group. Write the amounts in the boxes.

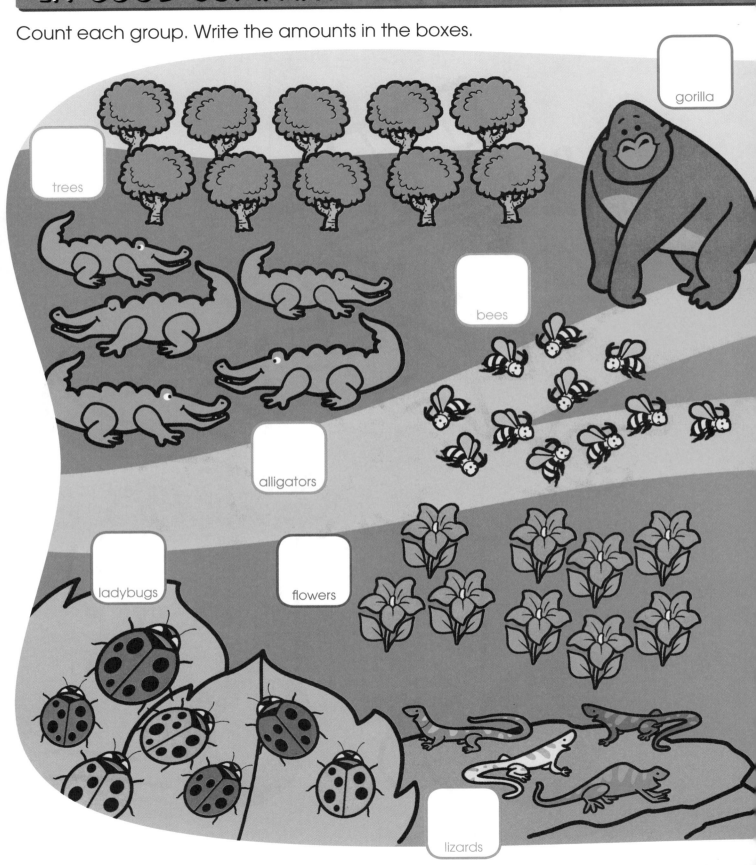

gorilla

trees

bees

alligators

ladybugs

flowers

lizards

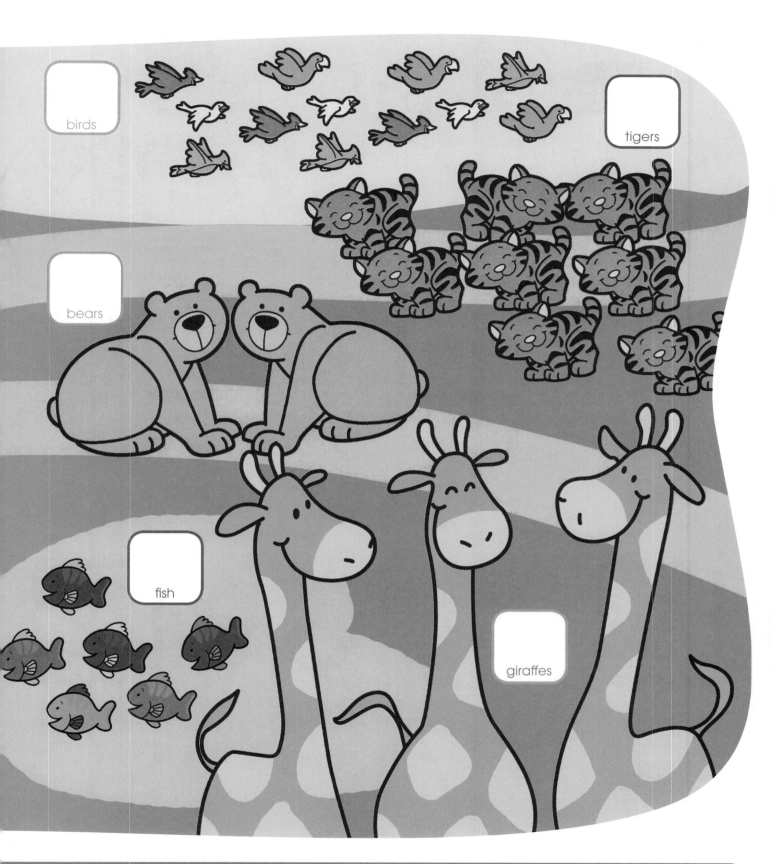

birds

tigers

bears

fish

giraffes

Reviewing the Numbers 1–12

MISSING NUMBER MYSTERY

Help solve the mystery of the missing numbers!
Write in the missing numbers.

4 5 6 7 9 9

7 8 9 10 11 12

1 2 3 4 5 6

3 4 5 6 7 8

5 6 7 8 9 10

Practicing Number Sequencing

©School Zone Publishing Company

FLYING BEFORE

Which number comes before?

1 2 3

1 comes **before** 2.

Write the number that comes **before**.

2 | 3 4

6 | 7 8

9 | 10 11

4 | 5 6

7 | 8 9

10 | 11 12

Practicing Number Sequencing: Concept of *Before*

Crayon Page! ✏️

Which number comes between?

1 2 3

2 comes **between** 1 and 3.

Write the number that comes **between**.

2 ☐ **4**   **3** ☐ **5**

5 ☐ **7**   **8** ☐ **10**

9 ☐ **11**   **10** ☐ **12**

Practicing Number Sequencing: Concept of *Between*   ©School Zone Publishing Company

RUNNING AFTER

Crayon Page!

Which number comes after?

3 comes **after** 2.

Write the number that comes **after**.

©School Zone Publishing Company

Practicing Number Sequencing: Concept of *After*

MORE FISH

Which tank has more fish?
Count the fish in each tank.
Write the amounts in the boxes.
Circle the tank that has **more** fish.

More means
a **bigger** number.

234

Learning the Concept of *More*

©School Zone Publishing Company

GREATER GROUPS

Crayon Page!

Which group has more people in it?
Count the people in each group.
Write the amounts in the boxes.
Circle the number that is **greater**.

Greater means **more than**.

Learning the Concept of Greater

FEWER RIDERS

Which ride has fewer riders?
Count the people on each ride.
Write the amounts in the boxes.
Circle the ride that has **fewer** riders.

Fewer means a **smaller** number.

236

Crayon Page!

Which group has fewer people in it?
Count the people in each group.
Write the amounts in the boxes.
Circle the number that is **less**.

Less means **not as many**.

237

Learning the Concept of *Less*

SAME STRIPES

Which zebras are the same?
Count the number of stripes on each zebra.
Place the matching zebra sticker next to each zebra.

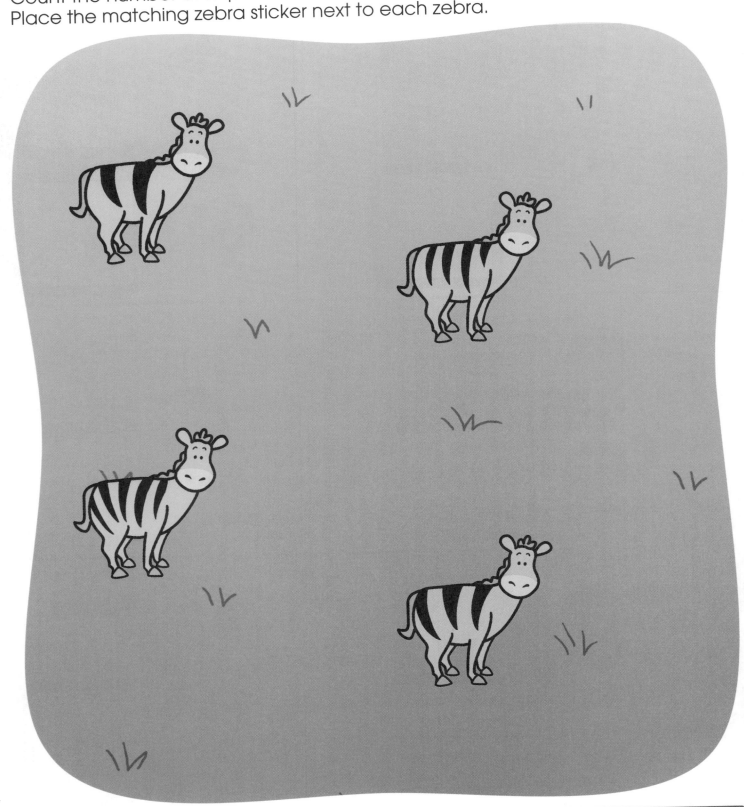

Learning the Concept of *Same*

SAME SNACKS

Help the concession stand workers put together lunch orders.

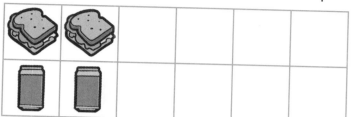

How many s?   1   ②   3

How many s?   1   ②   3

Place stickers to show the same number of s as s.

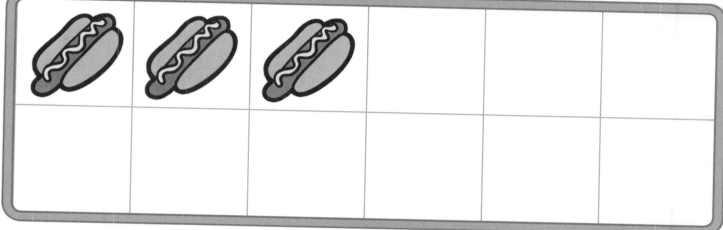

How many s?   2   3   4   How many s?   2   3   4

Place stickers to show the same number of s as s.

How many s?   4   5   6   How many s?   4   5   6

Learning the Concept of Same

COUNTING COINS

Crayon Page! ✏️

front   **back**

A **penny** is **one cent**.
I penny = I¢

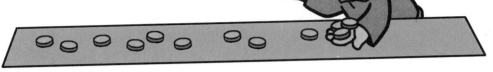

Practice counting pennies.
Count the pennies.
Write the amounts in the boxes.

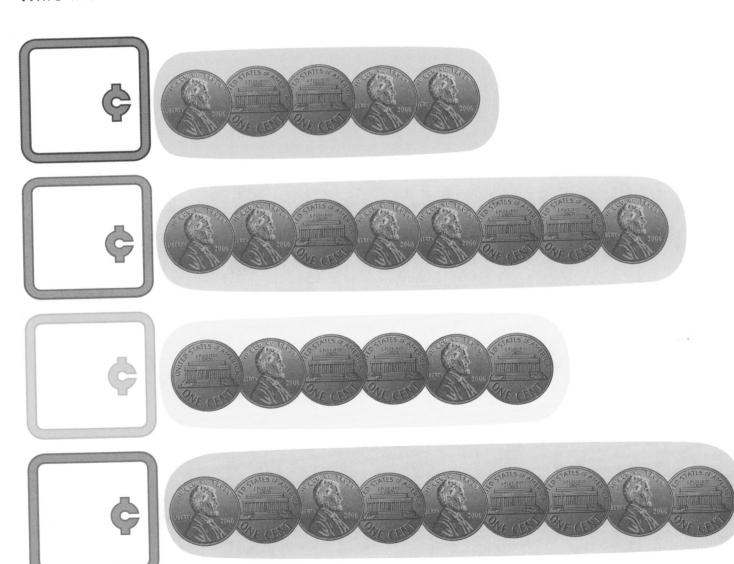

¢

¢

¢

¢

240

Counting Money

©School Zone Publishing Company

See what you can buy from the gift shop.

Count the pennies.
Draw a line from the pennies to the item that costs the same amount.

Counting Money

Which piggy bank has more money in it?
Circle the piggy bank that has **more** money.

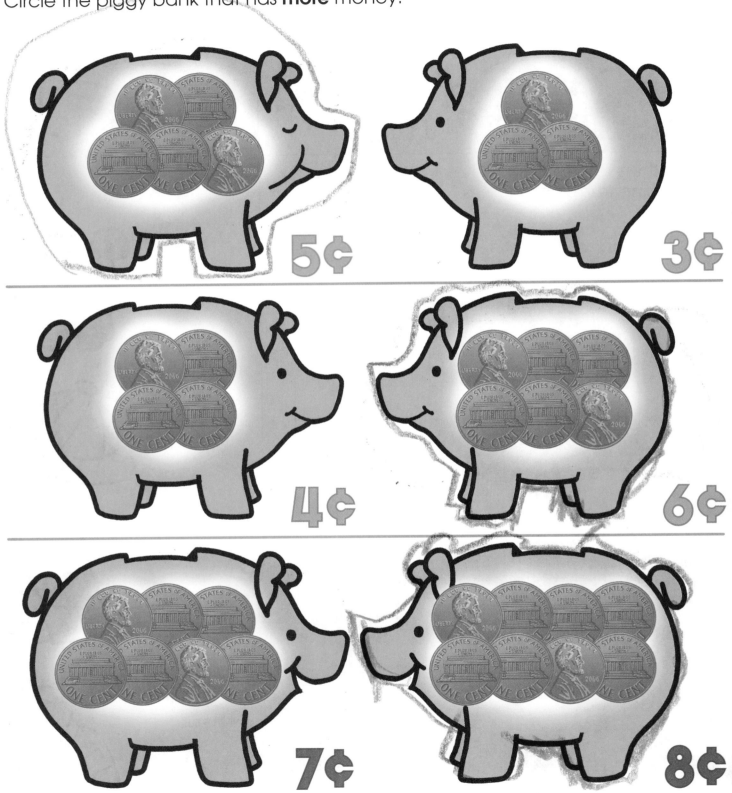

5¢

3¢

4¢

6¢

7¢

8¢

Counting Money; Concept of *More*

Which wallet has less money in it?
Circle the wallet that has **less** money.

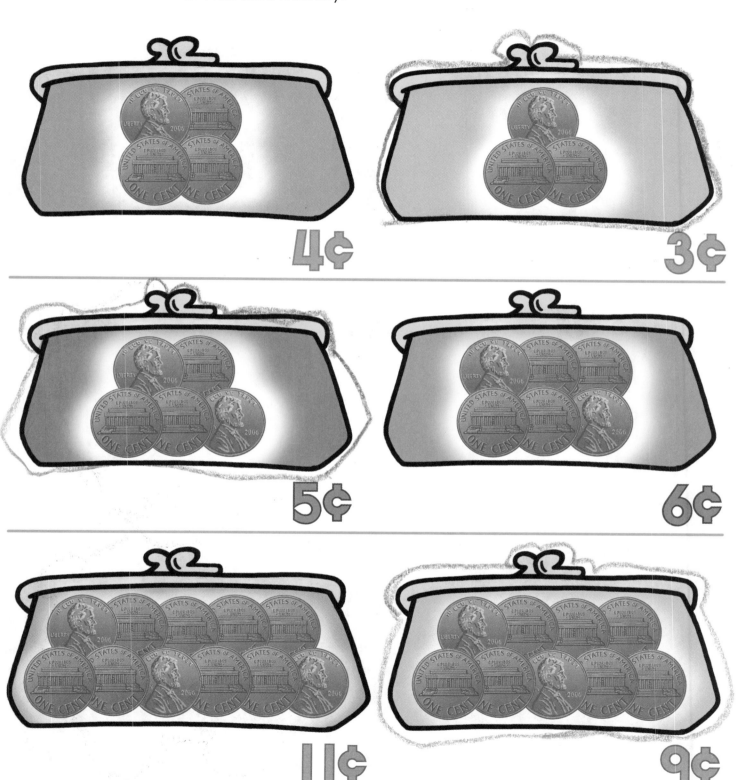

4¢

3¢

5¢

6¢

11¢

9¢

Counting Money; Concept of *Less*

The big clock in the middle of the park is missing some numbers.
Fill in the missing numbers by placing the number stickers on the clock.

Learning to Tell Time

TICKET TIME

A clock has two hands.
The short hand is called the **hour hand**.
The long hand is called the **minute hand**.

When the minute hand points to the twelve, we say o'clock. The hour hand is pointing to the two. It is 2 o'clock.

2:00

Today's Events

1:00 Park Tour

3:00 Dolphin Show

5:00 Parade

6:00 Air Show

Practice telling time.
Write the times that are shown.

Learning to Tell Time

SHOWTIME

Look at the times written below the clocks.
Use the hour hand stickers to make the clocks show those times.

2:00

4:00

7:00

8:00

Learning to Tell Time

The clocks in the gift shop are all mixed up.
How many clocks are showing each time? Write the numbers in the boxes.

How many clocks say 3:00?

How many clocks say 6:00?

How many clocks say 9:00?

Learning to Tell Time

How many animals are there in all?
Write the number to solve each problem.
The first one is done for you.

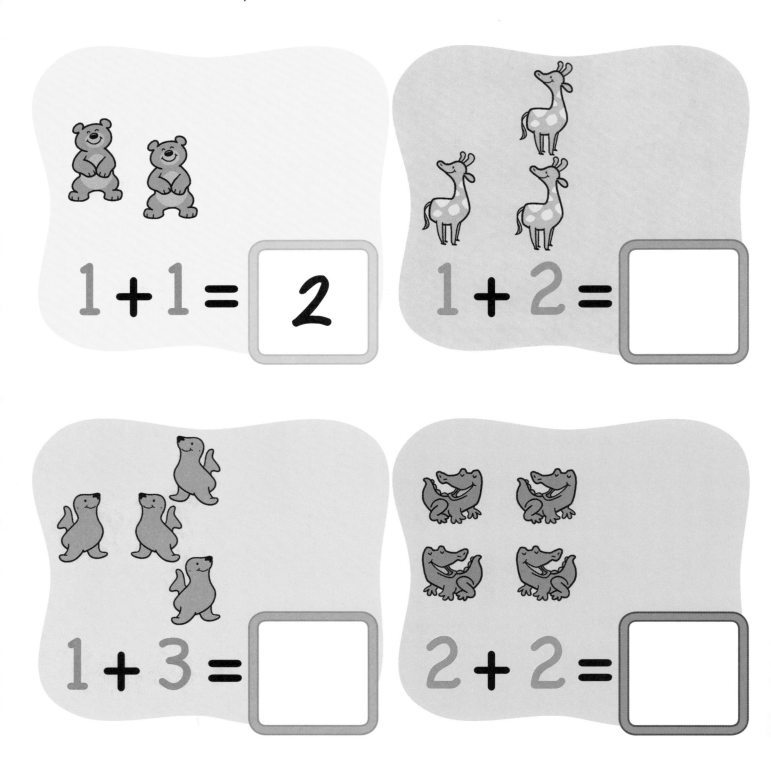

1 + 1 = **2**

1 + 2 =

1 + 3 =

2 + 2 =

How many flowers are there in all?
Write the number to solve each problem.

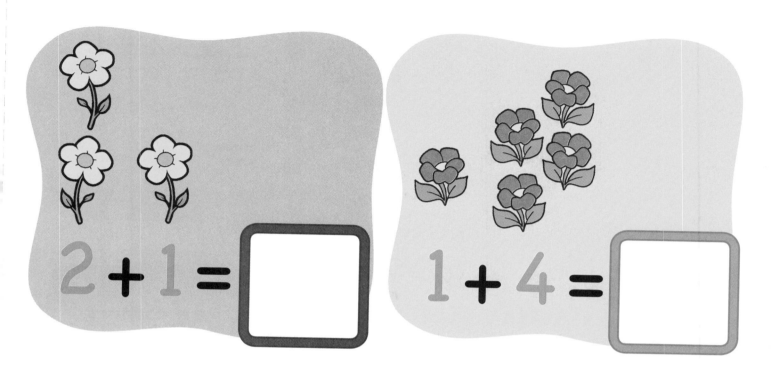

2 + 1 =

1 + 4 =

3 + 1 =

3 + 2 =

Learning to Add

RACING RIDERS

Help count the people on each ride.
Write the missing number in each addition problem.
The first one is done for you.

1 + 3 = 4

2 + 1 =

2 + = 4

Learning to Add

AWESOME AUDIENCE

Crayon Page!

Help count the people in each section of the theater.
Write the missing number in each addition problem.

$$1 + 4 = \boxed{}$$

$$2 + \boxed{} = 5$$

$$\boxed{} + 2 = 6$$

Learning to Add

ELEPHANTS EATING

Cross out the buckets of hay that were eaten.
Count how many buckets of hay are left.
Write the number.
The first one is done for you.

$2 - 1 =$ | 1

$3 - 1 =$

$4 - 2 =$

$3 - 2 =$

Learning to Subtract

©School Zone Publishing Company

MONKEYS MUNCHING

Crayon Page!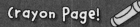

Cross out the bananas that were eaten.
Count how many bananas are left.
Write the number.

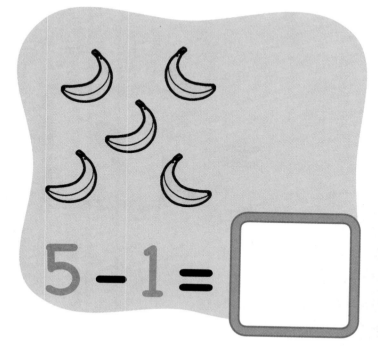

5 – 1 =

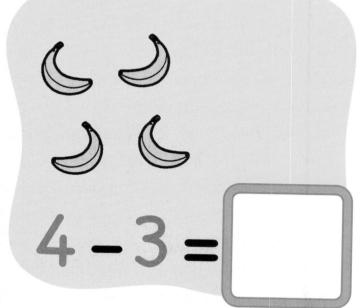

4 – 3 =

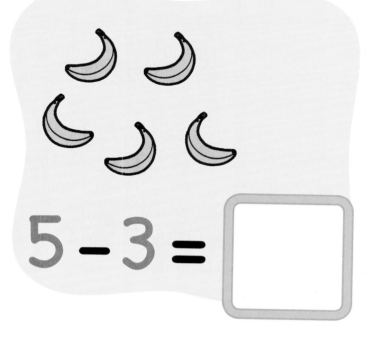

5 – 3 =

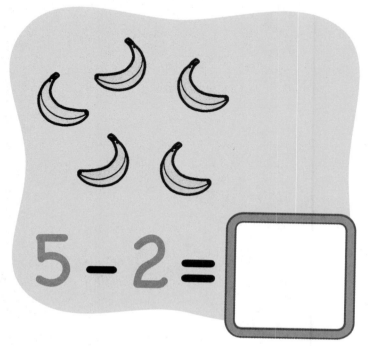

5 – 2 =

©School Zone Publishing Company

Learning To Subtract

BEDTIME AT THE ZOO

How many animals are still awake?
Write the number to solve each problem.
The first one is done for you.

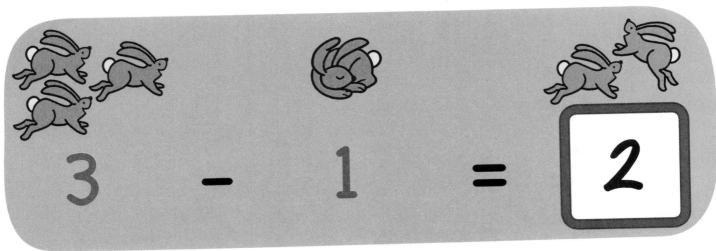

3   -   1   =   **2**

2   -   1   =

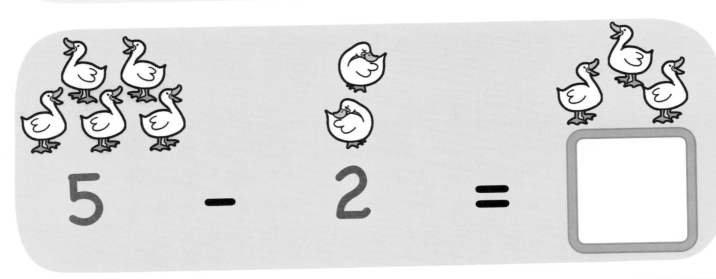

5   -   2   =

Learning to Subtract

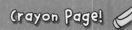

How many animals are still awake?
Write the number to solve each problem.

4 − 2 =

5 − 1 =

5 − 4 =

Learning to Subtract

CLOSING TIME

Follow the numbers from 1 to 12 to the end of the trail.
When you get to the end, place the sticker.

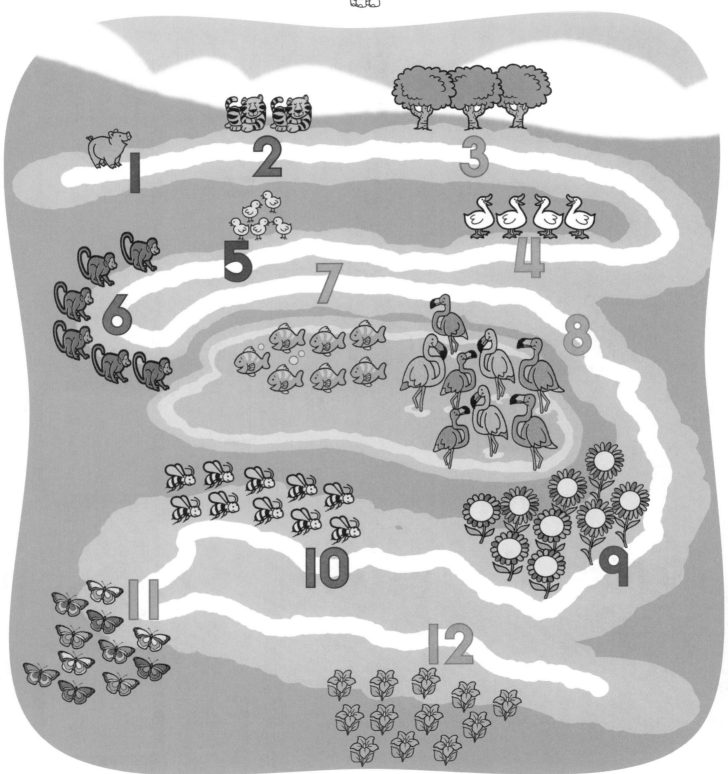

Reviewing the Numbers 1–12   ©School Zone Publishing Company

Which letter begins each picture's name?
Cut out the letters. Paste each letter next to the correct picture.

cut ✂

A B C D

Identifying Beginning Sounds

Which letter begins each picture's name?
Cut out the letters. Paste each letter next to the correct picture.

cut

E   F   G   H

Identifying Beginning Sounds

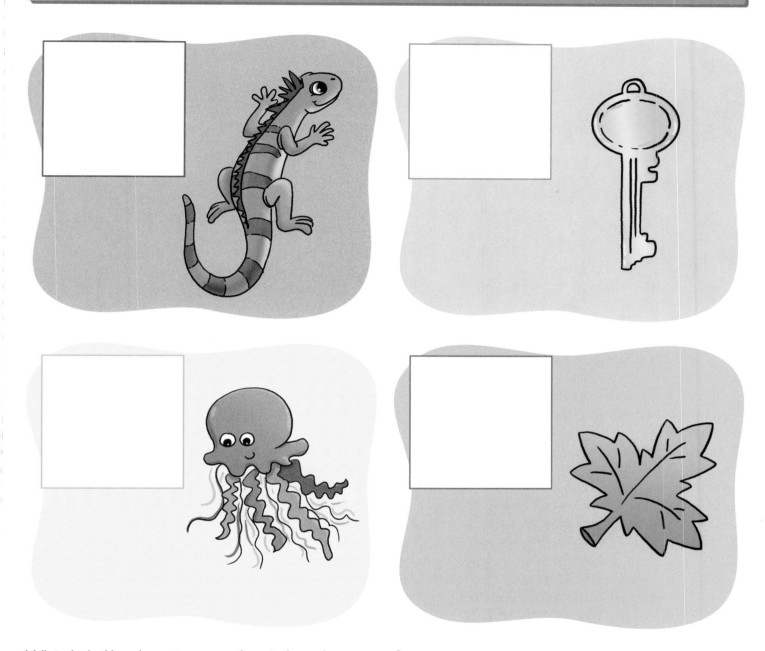

Which letter begins each picture's name?
Cut out the letters. Paste each letter next to the correct picture.

cut

I J K L

Identifying Beginning Sounds

Scissor Page! ✂

Which letter begins each picture's name?
Cut out the letters. Paste each letter next to the correct picture.

cut ✂

M N O P

Identifying Beginning Sounds

Which letter begins each picture's name?
Cut out the letters. Paste each letter next to the correct picture.

cut ✂

| Q | R | S | T | U |

Identifying Beginning Sounds

Which letter begins each picture's name?
Cut out the letters. Paste each letter next to the correct picture.

cut ✂

V W X Y Z

Identifying Beginning Sounds

Cut out the numbers. Paste each number next to the correct group.

cut

1   **2**   **3**   **4**

Matching Numbers to Groups

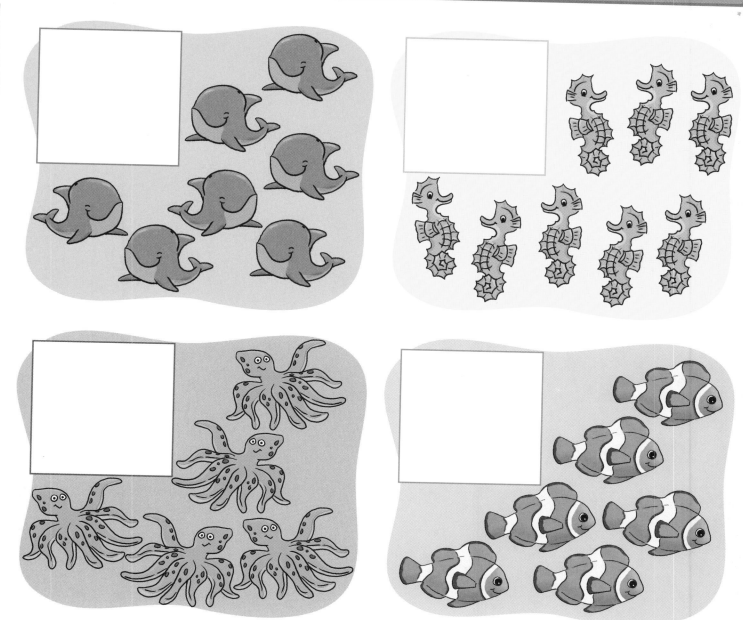

Cut out the numbers. Paste each number next to the correct group.

cut

5 6 7 8

Matching Numbers to Groups

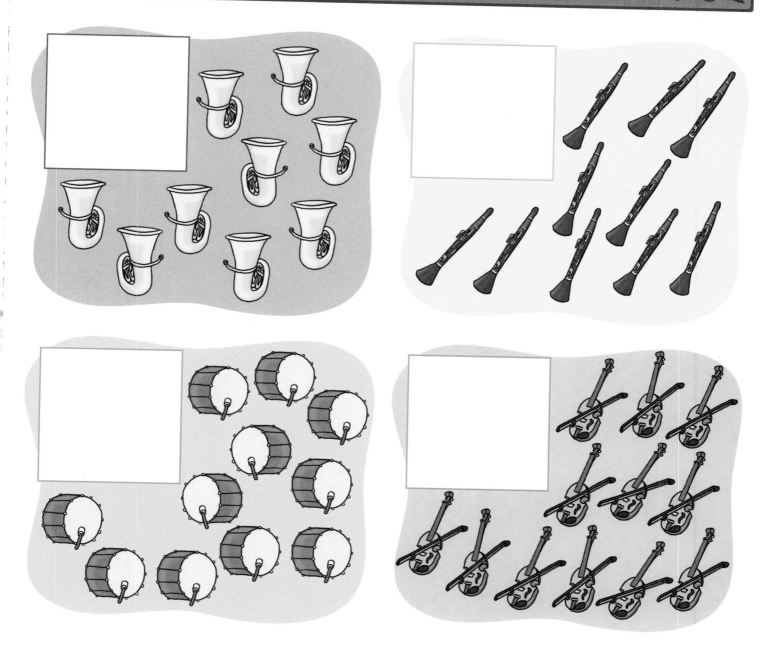

Cut out the numbers. Paste each number next to the correct group.

cut

9 10 11 12

Matching Numbers to Groups

ANIMAL PATTERNS

What comes next?
Cut out the pictures. Paste them to continue the patterns.

275

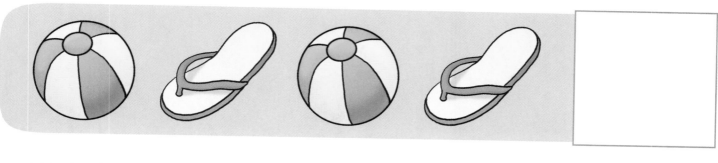

What comes next?
Cut out the pictures. Paste them to continue the patterns.

cut ✂

   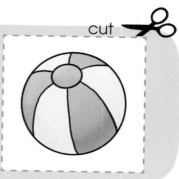

Extending Patterns

What comes next?
Cut out the pictures. Paste them to continue the patterns.

cut

Extending Patterns

A DAY AT THE CIRCUS

 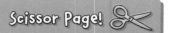

Cut out the puzzle pieces. Put the picture together.

cut

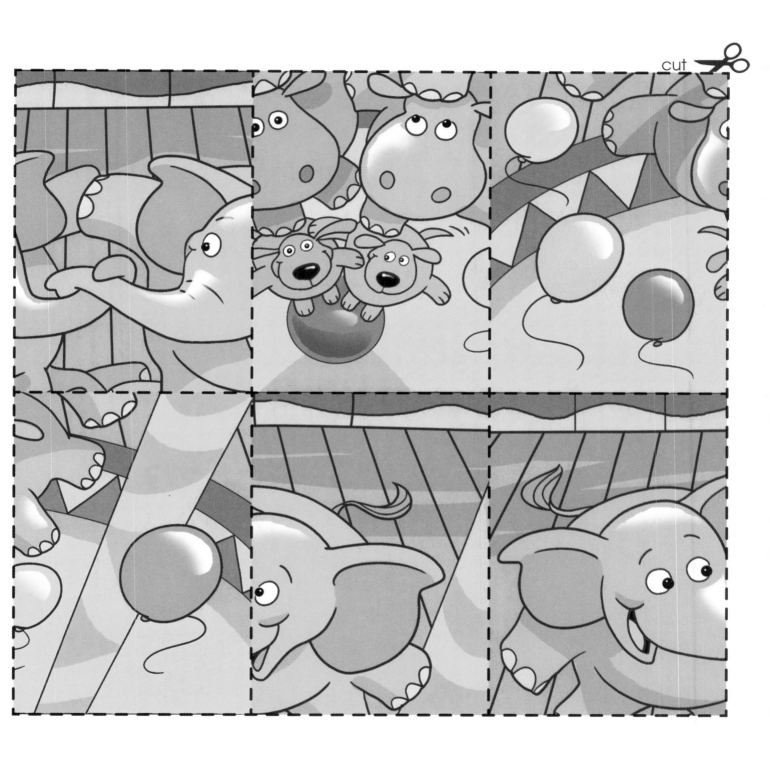

Circus Puzzle

PUMPKIN PATCH PLAY

Cut out the puzzle pieces. Put the picture together.

cut ✂

Farm Puzzle

BEDTIME STORY

Cut out the puzzle pieces. Put the picture together.

cut

©School Zone Publishing Company

Bedtime Puzzle

Page 1

Page 2

Page 3

Page 4

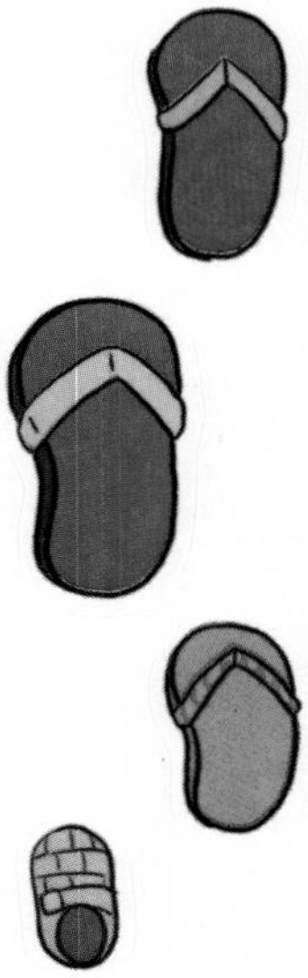

Page 7

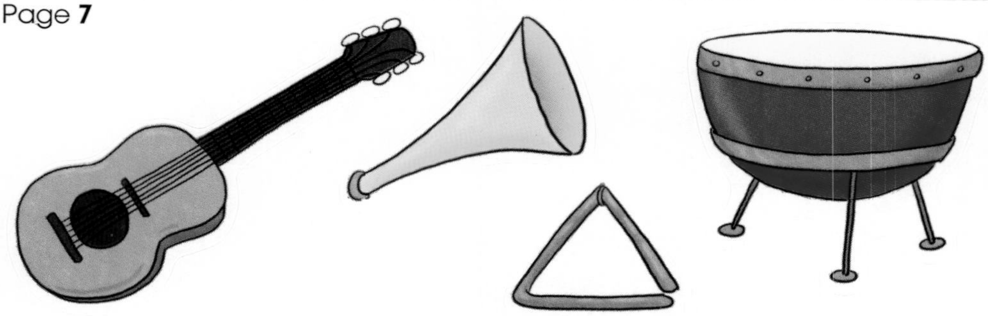

Page 8

Page 11

Page 12

Page 13

Page 14

Page 15

Page 16

Page 17

Page 18

Page 19

Page 21

Page 25

Page 28

1
4
2
5
3

Page 30

Page 32

Page 35

2 3 5
7 8 10

Page 38

Page 39

Page 40

Page 41

Page 43

Page 44

Page 46

Page 48

Page 53

cat
cow
dog
goat

Page 54

hat

frog

pear

boat

Page 57

Page 59

Page 60

Page 61

Page 62

Page 63

Page 64

Page 98

Page 99

Page 100

Page 101

Page 102

Page 103

Page 104

Page 105

Page 106

Page 107

Page 108

Page 109

Page 110

Page 111

Pages 142–143

Pages 144–145

Pages 146–147

Pages 148–149

Pages 150–151

Page 152

Even Pages 194–216

Page 195

Page 197

Page 199

Page 201

Page 203

Page 205

Page 207

Page **209**

Page **211**

Page **213**

Page **215**

Page **217**

Page **218**

1 2 3 4

Page **220**

5 6 7 8

Page **222**

9 10 11 12

Page **238**

Page **224**

Page **239**

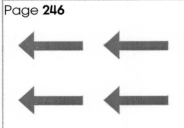

Page **244**

3 5 8 11

Page **246**

← ←

← ←

Page **256**